COSTING, REPORTS' & RETURNS

workbook

NVQ LEVEL 3
ACCOUNTING

David Cox and Michael Fardon,
with contributions by Janet Brammer and Roger Petheram

OSBORNE
BOOKS

Published by Osborne Books Limited
Unit 1B Everoak Estate
Bromyard Road
Worcester
WR2 5HN
Tel 01905 748071
Email books@osbornebooks.co.uk
www.osbornebooks.co.uk

Printed by the Bath Press, Bath

British Library Cataloguing in Publication Data
A catalogue record for this book is available from the British Library

ISBN 1 872962 53 X

CONTENTS

How to use this book

NVQ competences

workbook activities

Unit 6 - recording cost information

Unit 7- preparing reports and returns

Activities for Tutorial Chapters 9 to 13 are integrated in the three Assignments which start on page 64.

assignments

Unit 7 - preparing reports and returns

simulations

central assessment tasks

appendix – document formats

ACKNOWLEDGEMENTS

The authors wish to thank the following for their help with the compilation, reading and production of the text of this book: Jean Cox, Angela Davis, Catherine Fardon, Robert Fardon, Michael Gilbert, Rosemarie Griffiths and Jon Moore. Thanks are also due to Anita Sherwood of Hedgehog for the graphic designs on the cover and within the text.

Particular thanks go to Janet Brammer for contributing simulations and to Roger Petheram who has provided supplementary Central Assessment tasks, and has read and advised on the text.

The publisher is grateful to H M Customs & Excise for the provision of VAT Forms 100 which are Crown Copyright and are reproduced here with the permission of the Controller of Her Majesty's Stationery Office.

Osborne Books is greatly indebted to the Association of Accounting Technicians for their kind permission to reproduce simulations and Central Assessment tasks and also to the Lead Body for Accounting for permission to reproduce extracts from the Standards of Competence for Accounting.

HOW TO USE THIS BOOK

Costing, Reports & Returns Workbook is designed to be used alongside Osborne Books' *Costing, Reports & Returns Tutorial* and is ideal for student use in the classroom, at home and on distance learning courses.

Costing, Reports & Returns Workbook is divided into four sections: workbook activities, assignments, simulations and Central Assessment tasks.

workbook activities

Workbook activities are self-contained exercises which are designed to be used to supplement the activities in the tutorial text. Many of them are more extended than the exercises in the tutorial and provide useful practice for students preparing for simulations. There are no activities in this section for tutorial Chapters 9 to 13 which deal with the preparation of internal and external reports and returns. This is intentional: these areas are covered fully by the three full-length assignments in the next section. VAT, however, is given comprehensive treatment at the end of the workbook activities section.

assignments

These, as noted above, are self-contained sets of activities which extend learning and provide useful practice for the simulations which follow. In this workbook they are confined to the requirements of Unit 7 'Preparing Reports and Returns' Elements 1 and 2.

simulations

There are five full-length simulations in this workbook: three for Unit 6 and two for Unit 7. Two of these simulations have been issued by AAT and are reproduced with their kind permission. The other three simulations have been newly written for this workbook. Many of the documents and forms needed for the tasks are printed within the text and may be written in.

Central Assessment tasks

Osborne Books is grateful to AAT for their kind permission to reproduce the material in this section. The tasks for each Central Assessment are set out consecutively, because the material is inter-dependent and cross-referenced. The tasks, however, may be carried out on separate occasions, and do not necessarily have to be time constrained.

answers

Answers are not provided in the text. A Tutor Pack is available separately. Please telephone Osborne Books on 01905 748071 for details.

NVQ COMPETENCES

UNIT 6: RECORDING COST INFORMATION

element 1

record and analyse information relating to direct costs

❏   direct costs are identified in accordance with the organisation's costing procedures

❏   information relating to direct costs is clearly and correctly coded, analysed and recorded

❏   direct costs are calculated in accordance with the organisation's policies and procedures

❏   standard costs are compared against actual costs and any variances are analysed

❏   information is systematically checked against the overall usage and stock control practices

❏   queries are either resolved or referred to the appropriate person

element 2

record and analyse information relating to the allocation, apportionment and absorption of overhead costs

❏   data are correctly coded, analysed and recorded

❏   overhead costs are established in accordance with the organisation's procedures

❏   information relating to overhead costs is accurately and clearly recorded

❏   overhead costs are correctly attributed to producing and service cost centres in accordance with agreed methods of allocation, apportionment and absorption

❏   adjustments for under or over recovered overhead costs are made in accordance with established procedures

❏   standard costs are compared against actual costs and any variances are analysed

❏   methods of allocation, apportionment and absorption are reviewed at regular intervals in discussions with senior staff, and agreed changes to methods are implemented

❏   staff working in operational departments are consulted to resolve any queries in the data

element 3

prepare and present standard cost reports

❏   standard cost reports with variances clearly identified are presented in an intelligible form

❏   unusual or unexpected results are identified and reported to managers

❏   any reasons for significant variances from standard are identified and the explanations presented to management

❏   the results of the analysis and explanations of specific variances are produced for management

❏   staff working in operational departments are consulted to resolve any queries in the data

UNIT 7: PREPARING REPORTS AND RETURNS

element 1

prepare and present periodic performance reports

❑ information derived from different units of the organisation is consolidated into the appropriate form

❑ information derived from different information systems within the organisation is correctly reconciled

❑ when comparing results over time an appropriate method, which allows for changing price levels, is used

❑ transactions between separate units of the organisation are accounted for in accordance with the organisation's procedures

❑ ratios and performance indicators are accurately calculated in accordance with the organisation's procedures

❑ reports are prepared in the appropriate form and presented to management within required timescales

element 2

prepare reports and returns for outside agencies

❑ relevant information is identified, collated and presented in accordance with the conventions and definitions used by outside agencies

❑ calculations of ratios and performance indicators are accurate

❑ authorisation for the despatch of completed reports and returns is sought from the appropriate person

❑ reports and returns are presented in accordance with outside agencies' requirements and deadlines

element 3

prepare VAT returns

❑ VAT returns are correctly completed using data from the appropriate recording systems and are submitted within the statutory time limits

❑ relevant inputs and outputs are correctly identified and calculated

❑ submissions are made in accordance with current legislation

❑ guidance is sought from the VAT office when required, in a professional manner

coverage of NVQ specifications

The Osborne Books *Costing, Reports & Returns Tutorial* and *Costing, Reports & Returns Workbook* between them cover the performance criteria set out above. For coverage of the performance criteria by individual chapters, please see the introductory pages of the tutorial text.

NOTE ON UNIT NUMBERING
In 2000 the Unit numbers of the two NVQ Units covered in this book were changed. In effect the Unit numbers were each increased by one. These changes are reflected in the introductory pages of this book. References in subsequent pages should be adjusted accordingly.

Workbook Activities

This section contains activities which are suitable for use with the individual chapters of the Osborne Books *Costing, Reports & Returns Tutorial.*

Please note that activities for Chapters 9 to 13 of *Costing, Reports & Returns Tutorial* are not included in this section but are integrated in three Assignments which follow in the next section of this workbook (starting on page 64).

1 AN INTRODUCTION TO COST ACCOUNTING

1.1   (a)   Distinguish between cost units and cost centres.

       (b)   Suggest one cost unit and two cost centres for:

- a firm of accountants
- a parcel delivery company

1.2   The following cost codes are used by Proton Products Limited:

- depreciation, 700
- factory, 200
- office, 250

State the codes that will be used to charge depreciation to:

(a)   the factory cost centre

(b)   the office cost centre

1.3   Which one of the following is normally classed as a fixed cost for a manufacturing business?

(a)   raw materials to make the product

(b)   salaries of maintenance staff

(c)   production workers paid on the basis of work done

(d)   royalties paid to the designer of the product

Answer (a) or (b) or (c) or (d)

1.4   Which one of the following is normally classed as a variable cost for a 'high street' printing shop?

(a)   supervisor's salary

(b)   rent of shop

(c)   electricity used

(d)   cost of paper

Answer (a) or (b) or (c) or (d)

1.5   The following figures relate to the accounts of Manley Manufacturing Limited for the year ended 31 December 1999:

	£
Raw materials used in factory	75,280
Wages of production workers	69,180
Salaries of maintenance staff	30,950
Royalties paid to designer of product	15,110
Depreciation of factory plant and machinery	5,000
Electricity	4,160
Rent and rates	10,290
Salaries of office staff	38,450
Depreciation of office equipment	2,400
Sundry factory expenses	3,020
Sundry office expenses	1,590
Sales revenue	315,840

You are to:

(a)   Prepare a total cost statement for the year which shows:

•   prime cost

•   production cost

•   total cost

Discuss any assumptions that you make and state if you need further information from the company.

(b)   Prepare a profit statement for the year (on the assumption that all the goods manufactured have been sold).

Note: please see the Appendix (page 245) for specimen formats of a total cost statement and a profit statement.

1.6   Bunbury Buildings Limited makes garages and garden sheds which are pre-fabricated as a 'flat pack' in the factory to customer specifications.

You are working in the costing section of Bunbury Buildings and are asked to analyse the following cost items for May 1999 into the appropriate column and to agree the totals:

COST ITEM	TOTAL COST £	PRIME COST £	PRODUCTION OVERHEADS £	ADMIN COSTS £	SELLING AND DISTRIBUTION COSTS £
Wages of employees working on pre-fabrication line	19,205				
Supervisors' salaries	5,603				
Materials for making pre-fabricated panels	10,847				
Cleaning materials for factory machinery	315				
Hire of specialist equipment for one particular job	454				
Sundry factory expenses	872				
Salaries of office staff	6,091				
Repairs to sales staff cars	731				
Depreciation of office equipment	200				
Magazine advertising	1,508				
Sundry office expenses	403				
Hire of display stands used at garden centres	500				
Office stationery	276				
TOTALS	47,005				

2 MATERIALS COSTS

2.1 (a) Suggest:

- two ordering costs
- two stock holding costs

for a business that holds a stock of stationery for its own use.

(b) Calculate the Economic Order Quantity (EOQ) from the following information for boxes of 500 C5 envelopes:

- annual usage   200 boxes
- unit cost   £6.00 per box
- ordering cost   £30.00 per order
- stock holding cost   20 per cent of average stock value

Note:

The formula for EOQ is $\sqrt{\dfrac{2 \times \text{annual usage} \times \text{ordering cost}}{\text{unit cost} \times \text{stock holding cost}}}$

2.2 (a) Explain the principles of Just-In-Time (JIT) delivery systems and give one example for a manufacturing business and one example for a service business.

(b) What are the factors that a business should consider before using JIT for delivery of its purchases from suppliers?

2.3 You are providing accounting help to a friend who has recently set up in business making garden seats and tables. He understands the need to keep records of the different types of timber he has in stock. He has heard of the terms 'first in, first out' and 'last in, first out'; however, he thinks they refer to the physical movement of stock and are not relevant to the pricing of issues to production.

You are to explain by means of a memorandum:

- why FIFO and LIFO are used to price issues of materials
- whether or not FIFO and LIFO relate to the physical movement of stock

2.4 The supplies department of Peoples Bank has the following movements of an item of stock for June 1999:

		units	cost per unit £	cost £
1 June	Balance	2,000	2.00	4,000
15 June	Receipts	1,800	2.50	4,500
21 June	Issues	3,000		

You are to complete the following table for FIFO and LIFO:

DATE 1999	DESCRIPTION	FIFO £	LIFO £
21 June	Total issue value		
30 June	Total closing stock value		

2.5 Wyezed Limited manufactures a product using two types of materials, Wye and Zed. The accounting policy of the company is to issue material Wye to production using a FIFO basis, and material Zed on a LIFO basis.

The following are the stock movements of materials during the month of August 1999:

Material Wye – FIFO basis

1999		units	cost per unit £
1 Aug	Balance	5,000	5.00
10 Aug	Receipts	2,000	5.25
18 Aug	Receipts	3,000	5.50
23 Aug	Issues	8,000	

Material Zed – LIFO basis

1999		units	cost per unit £
1 Aug	Balance	10,000	4.00
6 Aug	Receipts	5,000	4.20
19 Aug	Receipts	6,000	4.40
24 Aug	Issues	12,000	

(a)   You are to complete the stores ledger records, below, for material Wye and material Zed.

STORES LEDGER RECORD

Material Wye

Date	Receipts			Issues			Balance		
1999	Quantity	Price	Value	Quantity	Price	Value	Quantity	Price	Value
		£	£		£	£		£	£
1 Aug	Balance						5,000	5.00	25,000
10 Aug	2,000	5.25	10,500						
18 Aug	3,000	5.50	16,500						
23 Aug									

STORES LEDGER RECORD

Material Zed

Date	Receipts			Issues			Balance		
1999	Quantity	Price	Value	Quantity	Price	Value	Quantity	Price	Value
		£	£		£	£		£	£
1 Aug	Balance						10,000	4.00	40,000
6 Aug	5,000	4.20	21,000						
19 Aug	6,000	4.40	26,400						
24 Aug									

(b)   At 31 August 1999, the net realisable value of each type of stock is:

    • material Wye   £10,000

    • material Zed   £44,000

Show the amount at which stocks should be valued on 31 August 1999 in order to comply with standard accounting practice.

2.6   Wyevale Tutorial College is a private college which runs courses for local companies on business and management subjects. The stocks of paper used for photocopying course material are maintained on a FIFO basis at present. The College's accountant has suggested that a change should be made to using either the LIFO or the standard cost basis.

As an assistant in the costing section you have been asked to prepare information based on the stock movements of photocopying paper for February 1999 which are as follows:

1 February	Opening stock	100 reams* at £2.10 per ream
5 February	Issues	80 reams
10 February	Purchases	150 reams at £2.20 per ream
15 February	Issues	90 reams
18 February	Purchases	200 reams at £2.25 per ream
24 February	Issues	120 reams

                  * a ream is 500 sheets

The standard price has been set at £2.10 per ream.

You are to:

(a)   Complete the stores ledger record shown (see next page) for February, using the FIFO basis.

(b)   Calculate the closing stock value at 28 February using FIFO, LIFO, and standard cost; and then complete the following table:

Method	Closing stock valuation		
	Quantity (reams)	Price (£)	Value (£)
FIFO			
LIFO			
Standard cost			

STORES LEDGER RECORD

Photocopying paper (reams)

Date	Receipts			Issues			Balance		
1999	Quantity	Price £	Value £	Quantity	Price £	Value £	Quantity	Price £	Value £
1 Feb	Balance						100	2.10	210

(c) Write a short memorandum on behalf of the accountant, which explains the difference between the FIFO, LIFO and standard cost methods of stock valuation. The memorandum will be circulated to members of the College's Finance Committee for discussion and should include your recommendation of the method to be used to ensure that the courses run by the College are not undercosted.

3 LABOUR COSTS

3.1 Briefly describe *three* sources that are used to gather information about work done in order to make payment to employees.

3.2 Clock cards are used to calculate:

(a) the wages of employees who work on piecework

(b) the cost of direct materials

(c) the salaries of monthly paid employees

(d) the wages of hourly paid employees

Answer (a) or (b) or (c) or (d)

3.3 HSB Mouldings Limited makes cases for television sets at its modern purpose-built factory. The company uses standard hours produced to measure its labout output.

You are to explain what is meant by a standard labour hour produced.

3.4 An employee makes 160 units of product Exe, 100 units of product Wye, and 250 units of product Zed. The standard labour time allowance per unit is: Exe 5 minutes; Wye 6 minutes; Zed 4 minutes.

What is the number of standard labour hours produced?

(a) 24

(b) 35

(c) 40

(d) 44

Answer (a) or (b) or (c) or (d)

3.5 Renne Limited pays its employees on a time rate, with a rate per hour for a 35-hour week. There are two overtime rates: time-and-a-third for weekdays (rate 1), and time-and-a-half for weekends (rate 2). The details of three employees for last week are as follows:

Employee	Time rate per hour	Total hours worked	Overtime rate 1 (hours)	Overtime rate 2 (hours)
L Constantinou	£ 8.70	40	3	2
H Gunther	£ 9.00	38	–	3
J White	£10.20	42	5	2

You are to calculate how much each employee earned for the week.

3.6 Elend Limited, a manufacturing company, pays its production-line employees on a piecework basis, but with a guaranteed time rate. The details of three employees for last week are as follows:

Employee	Time rate per hour	Hours worked	Production	Piecework rate
J Daniels	£10.00	38	800 units	45p per unit
L Ho	£9.50	35	650 units	55p per unit
T Turner	£9.75	36	500 units	73p per unit

You are to calculate how much each employee earned for the week.

3.7 Brock and Company, a manufacturing business, pays its production-line employees on a time basis. A bonus is paid where production is completed faster than the standard hour output; the bonus is 50 per cent of the standard hours saved and is paid at the actual labour rate per hour. The details of four employees for last week are as follows:

Employee	Time rate per hour	Hours worked	Standard hour output	Actual production
H Hands	£10.50	35	50 units	1,950 units
A Khan	£11.75	37	60 units	2,200 units
T Shah	£11.00	38	50 units	2,000 units
D Smith	£10.80	40	60 units	2,490 units

Note: there were no overtime payments last week.

You are to calculate how much each employee earned for the week.

3.8   Harts Doors and Windows Limited is a manufacturer of double-glazed doors and windows. The company has three production departments – cutting, assembly, and finishing. Data relating to labour for a four-week period is given on the labour cost card below.

The company uses a bonus scheme whereby employees receive 50 per cent of the standard hours saved in each department paid at the actual labour rate per hour. This is not included in the actual wages cost (below), which shows actual hours multiplied by the actual wage rate. There have been no overtime payments.

LABOUR COST CARD			
for the four weeks ended 26 March 1999			
	CUTTING	**ASSEMBLY**	**FINISHING**
Actual wages cost (£)	6,210	4,214	2,268
Standard hours	556	420	290
Actual hours	540	430	270
Standard hours saved			
Bonus (£)			
Total labour cost (£)			

You are to calculate the total labour cost for each department.

3.9   The Production Manager at Chucky Chicken Limited, which produces ready-to-cook chicken dishes, has been talking with the Accountant (your boss) about the possibility of introducing a system of bonus payments for production-line employees.

The Accountant has asked you to draft a memorandum addressed to the Production Manager which sets out the merits of a bonus system for both the company and its employees.

3.10   You are the Accounting Technician at Three Oaks Printing Company. One of your tasks is to deal with aspects of the company's payroll. The following queries on this week's payroll have been left for you by the book-keeper:

(a)   We paid £400 as overtime to the production-line employees. Should this be treated as a direct or an indirect cost?

(b)   There was a machine breakdown in the binding department. As a consequence, production-line employees, who are normally paid on a piecework basis, were paid the time rate for the period of the stoppage, totalling £150. Should this be treated as a direct cost or an indirect cost?

4 EXPENSES

4.1 Terry Hands works for Acme Builders as a member of the direct labour force. However, he has spent the last two weeks re-decorating the company's offices.

How should his wages for this period be dealt with in the accounts? Why is this?

4.2 Classify the following costs (tick the appropriate column):

	capital expenditure	revenue expenditure
(a) building an extension to the administration office		
(b) cleaning materials for factory machinery		
(c) repair of office photocopier		
(d) directors' salaries		
(e) carriage inwards on new machinery		
(f) carriage inwards on raw materials		
(g) installation of computer system		
(h) insurance of computer system		
(i) installation of special wiring for computer system		

4.3   Classify the following costs (tick the appropriate column):

	DIRECT EXPENSES	INDIRECT EXPENSES	
		production overheads	non-production overheads
(a) royalties paid to designer of product			
(b) straight-line depreciation of factory machinery			
(c) office electricity			
(d) insurance of factory buildings			
(e) advertising			
(f) rent on factory			
(g) units of output depreciation of factory machinery			
(h) factory manager's car expenses			
(i) sales department administration			

4.4   Jarvis Trading Limited depreciates its vehicles at 25 per cent per year, using the reducing balance method.

A car for the sales department was bought on 1 January 1999 at a cost of £16,000.

You are to calculate the depreciation amounts for 1999, 2000 and 2001, and to show the residual value at 31 December 2001. (Note: the company's financial year end is 31 December.)

4.5   Cradley Castings Limited has recently bought a new casting machine for which the details are as follows:

CASTING MACHINE

Cost price on 1 January 1999	£20,000 (net of VAT)
Estimated life	4 years
Estimated production:	
1999	55,000 units
2000	50,000 units
2001	40,000 units
2002	35,000 units
Estimated scrap value at 31 December 2002	£2,000 (net of VAT)

The management accountant is unsure whether to depreciate the machine using:

•   the straight-line method

•   the units of output method

She asks you to calculate the depreciation amounts for each year using the two methods. (Note: the company's financial year end is 31 December.)

Explain whether the depreciation amounts will be listed as direct expenses or indirect expenses.

4.6   The production manager of 'Print 'n Go', a specialist short-run printing business, is considering the purchase of a new computer-linked scanner. The cost is likely to be £18,000 (net of VAT) and the scanner will have a life of approximately four years, after which it will have a trade-in value of between £2,000 and £2,500 (net of VAT). The production manager knows from past experience that such equipment has the most use, and will lose most value, in the early part of its life.

You are to write a memorandum (see stationery next page) to the production manager detailing:

•   the method of depreciation that could be used

•   an approximate rate that could be applied, showing appropriate workings

•   reasons for the choice of depreciation method

MEMORANDUM

To:

From:

Subject: **Date:**

4.7 In the graphs below, draw in the lines to show how fixed costs and variable costs behave with changes in the level of activity.

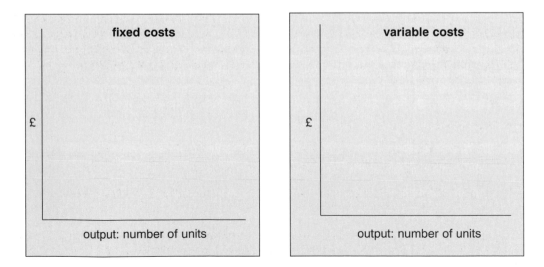

4.8 Classify the following costs (tick the appropriate column):

		FIXED	SEMI-FIXED	VARIABLE
(a)	rent of business premises			
(b)	week's hire of machinery at £100 per week for one particular job			
(c)	photocopier with a fixed rental and a cost per unit			
(d)	supervisor's wages			
(e)	reducing balance depreciation			
(f)	production-line employees paid a basic wage, with a bonus linked to output			
(g)	royalty paid to author for each book sold			
(h)	accountant's fees			
(i)	raw materials used in production process			

4.9 The research and development department of Castlemayne Limited, a design and engineering business, has recently developed a new type of electronic dispenser for serving exact quantities of beers, lagers and other drinks. The company has taken the decision to manufacture the product and you are helping the management accountant to prepare budgeted production costs at different levels of output of the new dispenser.

You have the following information in front of you:

- at 20,000 units of output, total budgeted costs are £350,000
- at 30,000 units of output, total budgeted costs are £500,000

The development manager has telephoned to ask the amount of budgeted fixed costs.

You are to use the 'high/low' technique to identify the element of fixed costs. You know from your involvement with the project that variable costs have a linear relationship, and that there are no stepped fixed costs.

4.10 Peter Parkinson is a central heating engineer who has designed a special type of thermostatic valve for use in domestic heating systems. He has decided to set up in business to manufacture the product and has carried out market research which suggests that demand for the product will be between 12,000 and 20,000 units each year.

Peter has budgeted the production costs on the basis of an output of 12,000 units as follows:

			£
variable costs	–	materials	36,000
	–	labour	24,000
	–	expenses	6,000
fixed costs	–	labour	18,500
	–	overheads	25,250

Peter asks you to prepare a schedule of budgeted production costs based on outputs of 12,000 units, 15,000 units and 20,000 units each year. The schedule is to show total production cost and the cost per unit at each level of output. (Note: you may assume that there is a linear relationship for variable costs, and that there are no stepped fixed costs.)

Briefly describe and explain the trend in costs per unit for the three budgeted levels of production.

5 OVERHEADS

5.1 Mereford Management College is a private college that has two teaching departments – accountancy and management.

The College charges overheads on the basis of lecturer hours. The following overhead analysis information is available to you (note that support services overheads – such as the administration office, reprographics department and learning resources – have already been apportioned to the teaching departments):

OVERHEAD ANALYSIS SHEET		
for January 1999		
	Accountancy Department	Management Department
Budgeted total overheads (£)	22,143	17,251
Budgeted lecturer hours	1,525	1,300
Budgeted overhead absorption rate (£)		

Details of a particular course – 'Finance for Managers' – that is taught in both the accountancy and management departments are as follows:

OVERHEAD ANALYSIS SHEET		
Course: Finance for Managers		
	Accountancy Department	Management Department
Lecturer hours	45	20
Budgeted overhead absorption rate (£)		
Overhead absorbed by course (£)		

You are to:

(a) calculate the overhead absorption rate for each of the two departments and complete the overhead analysis sheet

(b) calculate the overhead absorbed by the Finance for Managers course and complete the course overhead analysis sheet

(c) suggest an alternative overhead absorption rate that the College might use and comment on the circumstances that would make it appropriate

5.2 Wyevale Processing Limited processes and packs fruit and vegetables for supermarkets. The company has five departments – processing, packing, quality assurance, stores and maintenance.

The cost accountant has given you an overhead analysis schedule (see next page) to complete for next month.

The following information is available:

	Processing	Packing	Quality Assurance	Stores	Maintenance
Floor area (square metres)	160	210	50	80	100
Employees (number)	10	14	2	2	2
Machine usage (hours)	300	100	40		
Materials requisitions (number)	50	60	12		5
Maintenance hours (number)	60	50	20		

You are to:

(a) Prepare an analysis of budgeted production overheads for next month showing the basis of apportionment to the five departments of the business.

(b) Outline what now needs to be done with the budgeted costs of the service departments in order to arrive at overhead absorption rates for the production departments. Explain the reasons for this action.

5.3 Mercia Metals Limited is a manufacturing company with three production cost centres: forging, stamping and finishing. The following are the expected factory expenses for the forthcoming year:

	£
Rent and rates	14,625
Depreciation of machinery	8,000
Insurance of machinery	680
Supervisory salaries	42,790
Heating and lighting	4,420

Cost centre information is:

	Forging	Stamping	Finishing
Floor area (sq m)	400	600	300
Value of machinery	£30,000	£40,000	£10,000
Number of production-line employees	8	10	4

You are to:

(a) Apportion the expenses to the cost centres, stating the basis of apportionment.

(b) Calculate the overhead absorption rate (to two decimal places) of each cost centre, based on direct labour hours. Note that the company works a 35-hour week for 48 weeks a year.

BUDGETED PRODUCTION OVERHEAD SCHEDULE
for next month

Overhead	Basis of apportionment	Total £	Processing £	Packing £	Quality Assurance £	Stores £	Maintenance £
Rent and rates		4,500					
Supervisory salaries		3,690					
Depreciation of machinery		2,640					
Canteen costs		360					
TOTAL		11,190					

5.4 Wyvern Private Hospital has two patient wards – a day care ward for minor operations where the patients go home at the end of the day, and a surgical ward for patients who remain in the hospital for several days. There are two service departments – the operating theatre and administration.

The overheads of each department for last month were as follows:

		£
•	day care ward	28,750
•	surgical ward	42,110
•	operating theatre	32,260
•	administration	9,075

The basis for re-apportioning the overheads of the service departments is:

- operating theatre, on the number of operations carried out – day care ward, 160; surgical ward, 120

- administration, on the number of staff in each department – day care ward, 10; surgical ward, 25; operating theatre, 20

You are to use the step-down method to re-apportion the two service department overheads to the two patient wards.

5.5 Fox Furniture Limited makes tables and chairs for school and college use. There are two production lines – tables, and chairs – and two service departments – stores and maintenance.

The overheads of each department for last month were as follows:

		£
•	tables	12,000
•	chairs	8,000
•	stores	3,000
•	maintenance	2,000

The basis for re-apportioning the overheads of the service departments is:

- stores, on the number of requisitions – tables, 100; chairs, 80; maintenance, 20

- maintenance, on the value of equipment in each department – tables, £20,000; chairs, £18,000; stores, £2,000

You are to use the reciprocal method* to re-apportion the two service department overheads to the two production departments.

* use either the manual calculation or formulas, and round to the nearest pound

5.6   Steel Forgings (Rowcester) Limited is a heavy engineering business making parts for the car industry. The factory works a 35-hour week and is divided into three manufacturing divisions, with each making a different type of steel forging. Details of last week's production are as follows:

	Division 1	Division 2	Division 3
Direct materials	£3,260	£4,940	£8,760
Direct labour	£1,810	£2,525	£2,850
Number of production-line employees	5	8	10
Number of machine hours	150	250	300
Number of units produced	2,000	2,500	1,000

Production overheads were £10,000 for last week.

You are to:

(a)   suggest three different methods by which overheads can be absorbed, and calculate the appropriate overhead absorption rates

(b)   calculate the production cost per unit of output in each division using the three different methods of overhead absorption

(c)   compare the results of your calculations and suggest the most appropriate method of overhead absorption for this business

Note: where appropriate, round answers to the nearest penny

5.7   Activity based costing (ABC) is often suggested as an alternative to more traditional methods of overhead absorption. Explain how activity based costing differs from more traditional methods of overhead absorption, and the circumstances under which it is used.

5.8   A cost driver is a means of:

(a)   paying bonuses to delivery drivers

(b)   controlling the cost of direct labour

(c)   attributing overhead costs to activities

(d)   calculating the cost of direct materials

Answer (a) or (b) or (c) or (d)

6 METHODS OF COSTING

6.1 Wyvern Engineers Limited is a company which specialises in making parts for the car industry. The following Job Cost Sheet has been prepared by you, the Accounting Technician, for the actual costs of manufacture of a batch of gearbox casings for Mawgam Cars, a local specialist builder of touring cars:

		ACTUAL COSTS
JOB NO 471/99		
for gearbox casings		
Customer: Mawgam Cars		
1999		£
	Direct Materials	
8 Sep	MR 3141	422
10 Sep	MR 3152	286
10 Sep	MRN 58	(145)
	Direct Labour	
10 Sep	Wages analysis (30 hours)	420
	Direct Expenses	
8 Sep	Engineer's fee	250
	Production Overheads	345
	TOTAL COST	1,578

Note: Wyvern Engineers uses a labour hour rate for absorbing production overheads.

Your assistant asks you to explain the following about the Job Cost Sheet:

(a)   What does the transaction 'MR 3141' on 8 September mean?

(b)   What does the transaction 'MRN 58' on 10 September mean?

(c)   Where has the information on direct labour hours come from?

(d)   Why is the engineer's fee shown as a direct expense?

(e)   What is the absorption rate for production overheads?

6.2 OB Printers has been asked by John Dun, a local poet, to quote for the cost of printing a small book of poetry. John Dun is not sure how many copies to order, and has asked for quotations for 500, 1,000 and 2,000 copies.

The estimates by OB Printers are as follows:

Setting up the printing machine:	6 hours at £10.00 per hour
Artwork:	7 hours at £12.00 per hour
Typesetting:	20 hours at £15.00 per hour
Paper (for 500 copies):	£100.00
Other printing consumables (for 500 copies):	£50.00
Direct labour (for 500 copies):	5 hours at £13.00 per hour
Production overheads:	80% of direct labour costs
Profit:	25% on cost price

You are to:

(a) prepare the Job Cost Sheet (see next page) for 500, 1,000 and 2,000 copies, and also show the selling prices

(b) calculate the cost per book (to the nearest penny) to the author at each of the three different production levels

(c) respond to John Dun who, on seeing the quotations, says:

"Why is the price per copy so high for 500 copies? I am a starving poet, and I can't afford to have a large quantity printed. If the book sells well I shall regret not having had 2,000 copies printed."

JOB NO 12345

Poetry book for John Dun

	NUMBER OF COPIES		
	500	1,000	2,000
	£	£	£
Fixed Costs			
Setting up machine			
Artwork			
Typesetting			
Direct Materials			
Paper			
Other printing consumables			
Direct Labour			
Production Overheads			
TOTAL COST			
Profit (25% of total cost)			
SELLING PRICE			

6.3   Tiffany Dresses specialises in making one-off wedding and bridesmaids dresses. The following is the Job Cost Sheet for a recent order:

	ESTIMATE	ACTUAL	VARIANCE
JOB NO 98/101			
Wedding Dress for Miss Sanderson			
	£	£	£
Direct Materials			
Silk Shantung:			
estimate 10 metres at £25 per metre	250.00		
Thai silk:			
estimate 4 metres at £30 per metre	120.00		
Direct Labour			
Cutting: estimate 3 hours at £8 per hour	24.00		
Machining: estimate 6 hours at £6 per hour	36.00		
Finishing: estimate 5 hours at £7 per hour	35.00		
Overheads			
Estimate 14 hours at £10 per hour	140.00		
TOTAL COST	605.00		
Profit (40% of total cost)	242.00		
SELLING PRICE	847.00		

Note: Tiffany Dresses uses a labour hour rate for absorbing overheads.

You are to:

(a)   Complete the actual cost column of the Job Cost Sheet on the basis of the following:

- 10.5 metres of Silk Shantung were used at £24 per metre
- 3.5 metres of Thai silk were used at £38 per metre
- cutting took 3.5 hours at £8 per hour
- machining took 7 hours at £6.50 per hour
- finishing took 4 hours at £6.50 per hour

(b)   Show the variances (and whether they are adverse or favourable) and the actual profit (or loss) made on this job.

6.4 A manufacturer of security alarms has the following information concerning the first month of production:

	£
direct materials	10,725
direct labour	6,600
production overheads	3,900
security alarms completed	2,750
security alarms in progress	500

The work-in-progress is complete as regards materials, but is 50% complete as regards direct labour and production overheads.

You are to:

(a) complete the schedule below in order to calculate the cost per security alarm for the first month's production

(b) calculate the month-end valuation for work-in-progress

Note: use the average cost basis for your calculations

Cost element	Costs	Completed	Work-in-progress			Total	Cost	WIP
		Units	Units	% complete	Equivalent Units	Equivalent Units	per Unit	valuation
	A	B	C	D	E	F	G	H
					C x D	B + E	A ÷ F	E x G
	£						£	£
Direct materials								
Direct labour								
Production overheads								
Total								

6.5 At the beginning of January, Processing (Rowcester) Limited had 5,000 units in process. The costs of this work-in-progress were made up as follows:

		£
direct materials		19,500
direct labour		7,345
production overheads		8,500

During January a further 20,000 units were put into the process, with additional costs of:

		£
direct materials		79,000
direct labour		36,300
production overheads		42,025

At the end of January, 18,000 units had been fully processed, and 7,000 units remained in process. The closing work-in-progress was complete as regards direct materials, and 50% complete as regards direct labour and overheads.

You are to complete the schedule below in order to:

(a)   calculate the cost per unit for completed output in January

(b)   calculate the value of work-in-progress at the end of January

Note: use the average cost basis for your calculations

Cost element	Costs	Completed	Work-in-progress			Total	Cost	WIP
		Units	Units	% complete	Equivalent Units	Equivalent Units	per Unit	valuation
	A	B	C	D	E	F	G	H
					C x D	B + E	A ÷ F	E x G
	£						£	£
Direct materials								
Direct labour								
Production overheads								
Total								

7 STANDARD COSTING

7.1 Write short notes distinguishing between:

(a)   the ideal standard

(b)   the attainable standard

Which of these standards is of more use to managers?

7.2 Martley Manufacturing Company makes a product called 'Delta'. The company uses a standard costing system and the standard cost of making one unit of Delta in production week 12 is as follows:

direct materials

  – 4 kg of Alpha at £4.00 per kg

  – 3 kg of Beta at £5.00 per kg

direct labour

  – 0.5 hours in the moulding department at £10 per hour

  – 1.5 hours in the finishing department at £12 per hour

overheads

  – £4,000 for the week, which is to be recovered on the basis of direct labour hours

Budgeted production for the week is planned at 500 units of Delta.

You are to calculate the standard cost of producing one unit of Delta.

7.3 Perham Pots Limited makes a range of garden pots and ornaments. One of its products is called the 'Tuscany', for which the standard cost card is as follows:

STANDARD COST CARD			
Product: 'Tuscany' pot			
Cost element	*Performance standard*	*Standard rate/price*	*Standard cost*
Direct materials	1.5 kg	£0.40 per kg	£0.60
Direct labour	0.5 hour	£7.00 per hour	£3.50
Overheads:			
fixed	0.5 hour	£3.00 per hour	£1.50
variable	0.5 hour	£1.00 per hour	£0.50
		Cost per pot	£6.10

Note: overheads are recovered on the basis of direct labour hours.

You are to:

(a)   Complete the standard cost report (below) for an output of 550 'Tuscany' pots, using the information from the standard cost card, and calculate the standard cost and the total variance for each element of cost. Mark each variance either favourable (FAV) or adverse (ADV).

STANDARD COST REPORT

product	'Tuscany' pots	date	06.09.1999
budgeted output	500 pots	period	week 1
actual output	550 pots		September 1999

	standard cost			actual cost	variance
	cost per unit £	output	total cost £	£	£
materials		550		340.00	
labour		550		270 hours =1,971.00	
overheads:					
fixed		550		825.00	
variable		550		270.00	
TOTAL		550		3,406.00	

(b)   Analyse the direct labour cost variance into the appropriate sub-variances.

(c)   Suggest one reason for each of the sub-variances occurring and outline the corrective action that needs to be taken in each case.

(d)   Who would be responsible for taking the corrective action in (c) above?

7.4 The accounting procedures manual of Southern Industrials plc states that "managers should take action on reported variances that are both significant and controllable."

In the context of standard costing, you are to explain the terms 'significant' and 'controllable', and give examples of each.

7.5 Last week's standard cost report of Malham Manufacturing shows that:

- for direct material Exe there was an adverse materials price sub-variance, and a favourable materials usage sub-variance

- for direct labour in the moulding department, there was a favourable labour rate sub-variance, and an adverse labour efficiency sub-variance

You are to explain how:

(a)   the sub-variances for materials might be connected

(b)   the sub-variances for labour might be connected

7.6 The Production Manager of Shrawley Soft Toys Limited has asked you to review last week's labour costs on the 'Teddy Bear' production line. The details are:

Summary of labour costs: 'Teddy Bear' production

- Budgeted labour rate, £6.00 per hour

- Standard hours produced, 100

- Actual hours worked (including 4 hours of idle time caused by a machine breakdown), 110

- Actual labour cost, £687.50

You are to calculate:

(a)   labour rate variance

(b)   idle time variance

(c)   labour efficiency variance

(d)   total labour variance

7.7   Wyvern Leisure Limited makes plastic garden furniture. The following standards per unit have been set for the manufacture of garden tables in production week 15:

materials	4 kgs at £4.50 per kg
labour	0.5 hours at £8.00 per hour

The actual results for production week 15 were:

number of garden tables made	500
materials used	2,100 kgs, cost £9,030
labour	240 hours, cost £1,980

You are to:

(a)   calculate the total materials and labour variances for week 15

(b)   calculate the appropriate sub-variances for materials and labour for week 15

(c)   make a list of the managers responsible within the company who should receive a copy of the variances calculated in (a) and (b)

(d)   write a memo to the managers listed in (c) outlining the possible reasons for the variances that have arisen and advising as to what action should be taken

7.8 Tetbury Toys Limited specialises in making garden toys such as swings, slides, climbing frames, tree houses.

For production week 11, the company budgeted to make 250 climbing frames with the following standard prime cost:

STANDARD COST PER CLIMBING FRAME

	Quantity	Unit price	Cost per frame
Materials	20 metres of tubing	£1.00 per metre	£20.00
Labour	4 hours	£8.00 per hour	£32.00
Prime cost			£52.00

Actual production for the week was 260 climbing frames with the following actual costs:

ACTUAL COST – PRODUCTION WEEK 11

	Quantity	Total cost
Materials	5,600 metres of tubing	£5,040.00
Labour	1,010 hours	£8,585.00
Prime cost		£13,625.00

You are to:

(a) Calculate the following cost variances:

- – materials price variance
- – materials usage variance
- – labour rate variance
- – labour efficiency variance

(b)   Complete the table of variances which follows for materials and labour, and show the total prime cost variance.

VARIANCE SCHEDULE

PRODUCT: 260 climbing frames   **Period:** week 11

	£	£
Materials variances		
Price		
Usage		
Labour variances		
Rate		
Efficiency		

TOTAL PRIME COST VARIANCE

REPORT

Include a brief report that:

•   notes any significant sub-variances of £250 or more

•   suggests, from the information given, possible reasons for all materials and labour variances

7.9 Kyle Kitchenware Limited makes stainless steel kitchen equipment, such as bowls, knives and whisks.

Last week one of the production lines was making bowls of 250 mm diameter. The company budgeted to make 500 bowls with production overhead costs of:

fixed overheads	£1.00 per bowl
variable overheads	£0.60 per bowl

Overheads are absorbed on the basis of the number of direct labour hours.

The standard overhead cost of making 500 bowls was budgeted to be:

STANDARD COST (500 BOWLS)

fixed production overheads

125 hours at £4.00 per hour = £500.00

variable production overheads

125 hours at £2.40 per hour = £300.00

£800.00

As the overhead absorption rate is based on the number of direct labour hours:

- fixed overheads: 4 bowls per hour at £1.00 per bowl = £4.00 per hour
- variable overheads: 4 bowls per hour at £0.60 per bowl = £2.40 per hour

---

At the end of the week's production, it is found that 550 bowls have been produced. The actual cost of the overheads were:

ACTUAL COST (550 BOWLS)

fixed production overheads

130 hours at £4.20 per hour = £546.00

variable production overheads

130 hours at £2.20 per hour = £286.00

£832.00

You are to:

(a) Complete the extract which follows from the standard cost report for fixed and variable production overheads, based on an output of 550 bowls.

	standard cost			actual cost	variance
	cost per unit £	output	total cost £	£	£
overheads:					
fixed					
variable					

(b) Calculate the variances and sub-variances for overheads. Fixed production overhead variances may be ascertained by using the following bar charts:

BAR CHART 1

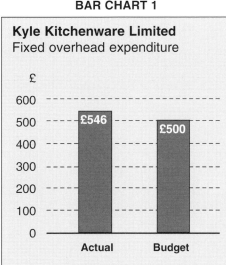

BAR CHART 2

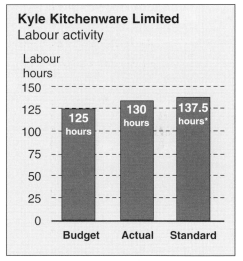

*137.5 hours = 125 hours x (550 bowls ÷ 500 bowls)

(c) Complete the table of variances which follows on the next page for overheads (materials and labour variances have already been recorded), including the total variance 'box'.

VARIANCE SCHEDULE

PRODUCT: 550 bowls (250 mm diameter)   **Period:** last week

		£		£	
Materials variances					
Price				25	ADV
Usage				10	FAV
				15	ADV
Labour variances					
Rate				20	ADV
Efficiency				60	FAV
				40	FAV
Variable overhead variances					
Expenditure					
Efficiency					
Fixed overhead variances					
Expenditure					
	Capacity				
	Efficiency				
Volume					
TOTAL VARIANCE					

REPORT

Include a brief report on the overhead variances (*note:* a report on materials and labour variances is not required).

report continuation

7.10 The Management Accountant of Marcle Manufacturing Limited has given you the following summary of the company's two departments for the last six months:

	Casting Department	Finishing Department
Budgeted production (hours)	18,400	7,850
Actual labour hours worked	18,550	7,390
Standard hours produced	18,700	7,650
Efficiency ratio		
Capacity ratio		
Activity ratio		

The Management Accountant asks you to calculate (to one decimal place) the efficiency, capacity and activity ratios for the two departments and to write a short memorandum on your findings.

8 BOOK-KEEPING FOR COSTING

8.1 In a manufacturing account, indirect materials and indirect labour form part of:

    (a)   prime cost

    (b)   production overheads

    (c)   non-production overheads

    (d)   indirect expenses

Answer (a) or (b) or (c) or (d)

8.2 Allocate the following costs (tick the appropriate column):

	manufacturing account	profit and loss account
(a) salaries of sales staff		
(b) wages of production-line employees		
(c) royalty paid to designer of product		
(d) straight-line depreciation of factory machinery		
(e) factory power costs		
(f) re-decoration of administration offices		
(g) units of service depreciation of photocopier in administration office		
(h) bank overdraft interest		
(i) overtime paid to production-line employees		

8.3   The following figures relate to the accounts of Middleton Manufacturing Limited for the year ended 31 December 1999:

	£
Stocks at 1 January 1999:	
Raw materials	25,250
Finished goods	12,380
Stocks at 31 December 1999:	
Raw materials	29,610
Finished goods	11,490
Expenditure during year:	
Purchases of raw materials	75,340
Factory wages – direct	54,690
Factory wages – indirect	22,330
Factory rent and rates	7,380
Factory power	4,250
Depreciation of factory machinery	2,500
Factory maintenance	1,870
Sundry factory expenses	1,140
Non-production overheads	46,730
Sales of finished goods	286,940

Note: Factory power is to be treated as a production overhead.

You are to prepare the year-end:

*   manufacturing account
*   profit and loss account

Note: please see the Appendix (page 245) for specimen formats of a manufacturing account and a profit and loss account.

8.4   The following figures relate to the accounts of Ryedale Limited, a manufacturing business, for the year ended 31 October 1999:

	£
Stocks of raw materials at 1 November 1998	41,210
Stocks of raw materials, 31 October 1999	46,380
Stocks of finished goods, 1 November 1998	29,470
Stocks of finished goods, 31 October 1999	38,290
Purchases of raw materials	311,050
Sales of finished goods	874,360
Rent and rates	35,640
Factory wages – direct	180,860
Factory wages – indirect	45,170
Factory power	12,040
Factory heat and light	5,030
Factory sundry expenses and maintenance	10,390
Administration salaries	154,610
Advertising	30,780
Office expenses	10,390
Depreciation of factory plant and machinery	12,500
Depreciation of office equipment	2,500

Additional information:

- factory power is to be treated as a production overhead
- rent and rates are to be allocated 75% to manufacturing and 25% to administration

You are to prepare the year-end:

- manufacturing account
- profit and loss account

Note: please see the Appendix (page 245) for specimen formats of a manufacturing account and a profit and loss account.

8.5   Shah and Company is a manufacturing business which uses an integrated book-keeping system for its costing and financial accounting.

At 1 January 1999, the first day of a new financial year, the company has a number of balances in its ledger as shown on the next few pages.

During January the following transactions took place:

	£
Direct materials bought on credit	12,500
Direct labour costs paid by cheque	10,500
Production overheads paid by cheque	4,000
Non-production overheads paid by cheque	5,000
Credit sales	38,000
Receipts from debtors	41,000
Paid to creditors	12,000
Direct materials transferred to work-in-progress	13,000
Work-in-progress transferred to finished goods	28,000
Finished goods transferred to cost of sales	27,000

You are to:

(a)   Record the above transactions in the integrated book-keeping system of Shah and Company, using the accounts on the next four pages, and show the net profit for the month. (Note that the full cost of direct labour and production overheads is to be transferred to work-in-progress.)

(b)   Show the trial balance at 31 January 1999, after preparing the profit and loss account in the double-entry accounts.

Dr		Capital Account		Cr
1999		£	1999	£
			1 Jan Balance b/d	40,000

Dr		Machinery Account		Cr
1999		£	1999	£
1 Jan Balance b/d		15,000		

Dr		Office Equipment Account		Cr
1999		£	1999	£
1 Jan Balance b/d		8,000		

Dr		Bank Account		Cr
1999		£	1999	£
1 Jan Balance b/d		5,500		

Dr   **Materials Account**   Cr

1999		£	1999	£
1 Jan	Balance b/d	3,500		

Dr   **Work-in-Progress Account**   Cr

1999		£	1999	£
1 Jan	Balance b/d	3,000		

Dr   **Finished Goods Account**   Cr

1999		£	1999	£
1 Jan	Balance b/d	4,000		

Dr   **Debtors' Account**   Cr

1999		£	1999	£
1 Jan	Balance b/d	5,000		

Dr   **Creditors' Account**   Cr

1999	£	1999	£
		1 Jan Balance b/d	4,000

Dr   **Labour Costs Account**   Cr

1999	£	1999	£

Dr   **Production Overheads Account**   Cr

1999	£	1999	£

Dr   **Non-Production Overheads Account**   Cr

1999	£	1999	£

Dr		**Sales Account**		Cr
1999	£	1999		£

Dr		**Cost of Sales Account**		Cr
1999	£	1999		£

Dr		**Profit and Loss Account**		Cr
1999	£	1999		£

8.6 Albion Limited, a manufacturing company, has three departments – moulding, assembly and finishing. The company uses a budgeted overhead absorption rate based on direct labour hours.

The following data relates to production week 46:

	Moulding Department	Assembly Department	Finishing Department
Actual overheads incurred	£1,246	£2,021	£912
Budgeted absorption rate per direct labour hour	£10.40	£12.80	£9.50
Actual direct labour hours worked	125	155	96
Overhead absorbed			
(Under-)/over-absorption of overheads			

You are to complete for each department:

(a) the table (above) to show the amount of overhead absorbed and the under- or over-absorption of overheads

(b) the production overheads accounts (below), including any transfer to profit and loss account

Dr	**Production Overheads Account: Moulding Department**		Cr
	£		£
Bank	1,246		

Dr	**Production Overheads Account: Assembly Department**		Cr
	£		£
Bank	2,021		

Dr	**Production Overheads Account: Finishing Department**		Cr
	£		£
Bank	912		

(c) What effect will this under- or over-absorption have on budgeted profits?

8.7 The data which follows relates to the finishing department of Bringsty Manufacturing. In this department overheads are recovered on the basis of machine hours.

Finishing Department Period ending 30 June 1999	
Budgeted overhead	£109,931
Budgeted machine hours	10,550
Budgeted overhead absorption rate	
Actual machine hours	10,350
Overhead absorbed	
Actual overhead	£114,592
(Under-)/over-absorption of overhead	

You are to:

(a) Complete the table above

(b) Write a memorandum to the Management Accountant which explains:

      the consequences of the results for the period

  – the possible causes

  – the effect on the costing of jobs which passed through the finishing department during the period

  – possible action to be taken for the future

8.8 For each of the following variances, indicate which book-keeping account will be debited or credited (tick the appropriate column):

Variance	Expense Account		Work-in-Progress Account	
	Debit	Credit	Debit	Credit
Favourable labour rate				
Adverse materials usage				
Favourable labour efficiency				
Adverse fixed production overhead expenditure				
Favourable variable production overhead efficiency				
Adverse idle time variance				

8.9 The accounts which follow are taken from the book-keeping system of Hopton Brewery Company. The accountant is in the process of completing the period-end cost accounts in respect of materials and labour: she has calculated the materials usage variance at £750 adverse, and the labour efficiency variance at £950 favourable. These, together with the materials price variance and the labour rate variance, have not yet been recorded in the accounts.

Dr		**Materials Account**		Cr
	£			£
Balance b/d	12,500	Work-in-progress		115,000
Creditors	110,000	Balance c/d		9,000

Dr		**Labour Costs Account**		Cr
	£			£
Bank	84,500	Work-in-progress		82,500

Dr		**Work-in-Progress Account**		Cr
	£			£
Balance b/d	15,500	Finished goods		197,000
Materials	115,000	Balance c/d		16,200
Labour	82,500			

Dr		**Variance Account**		Cr
	£			£

You are to complete the above accounts to show the variances at the period-end.

8.10 The following variances have been calculated for production week 45:

- materials price variance, £655 adverse
- materials usage variance, £200 favourable
- labour rate variance, £430 favourable
- labour efficiency variance, £110 adverse
- fixed production overhead expenditure variance, £275 favourable
- fixed production overhead efficiency variance, £185 adverse

You are to show how these will be recorded in:

- materials account
- labour costs account
- production overheads account
- work-in-progress account
- variance account, including any transfer to profit and loss account

Note: you are to draw up suitable double-entry accounts on your own stationery.

14 THE PRINCIPLES OF VAT

14.1 Various clients of the firm for which you work, knowing that you are an expert on VAT, ask you about VAT registration. The situations are as follows:

(a) David Backham set up in business exactly 12 months ago, but is not registered for VAT. His sales turnover for the year is £150,000.

(b) Jimmy Blacknap is setting up a limited company this week. He is importing sports cars from Europe and expects his sales for the first month to exceed £200,000.

(c) Alan Cutter is setting up a gardening services business this week and expects his sales for the first month to be approximately £45,000.

(d) Mick Owen is setting up a bookshop this month and expects to sell £150,000 worth of books in the first year of trading. He says that as books are zero-rated, it is hardly worth registering for VAT.

(e) Jenny Barnes is setting up a part-time business selling childrens clothes. She only expects to sell £2,000 of clothes each month. Should she register for VAT?

State what you would reply to these clients, advising them

• whether they have to register

• when they have to register

• any advantages which may result from their registering for VAT

14.2 You are working in the accounts office of a local manufacturing firm. You have been given a batch of invoices to prepare. Among them are five invoices for customers who are quoted a 5% cash discount for settlement within 7 days.

Calculate the VAT due (at the current rate) and the invoice total, using the following table:

invoice	net total (before VAT) £	VAT £	invoice total £
4563	1,265.75		
4567	456.25		
4571	5,678.90		
4575	45.60		
4578	415.50		

14.3 Monika Schmidt runs a fitness centre "Tone Up" based in the town. "Tone Up" is incorporated as a limited company and is VAT-registered. Monika also uses a room in her house as an office for business purposes; the telephone bills for her home line are apportioned 30% business use, 70% domestic use.

During one week the following VAT invoices are received by the business:

supplier	goods/services supplied	net amount £	VAT £	gross amount £
Janus Cleaning	Cleaning of fitness centre	192.00	33.60	225.60
Ergo Sports	Rowing machine	1,250.00	218.75	1,468.75
Wyvern Motors	Mazda MX5 sports car	16,579.50	2,901.41	19,480.91
Peters Restaurant	Entertaining clients	230.60	40.35	270.95
BT	Home telephone line	126.76	22.18	148.94
BT	Business telephone line	346.74	60.67	407.41
Forte Hotels	Hotel room on business trip	240.50	42.08	282.58
Zap Supplies	Business stationery	46.50	8.13	54.63

You are to calculate

(a) the total VAT that the business will be able to claim as input tax

(b) the VAT that Monika will have to pay

14.4 When is the tax point in the following circumstances? All dates are in the same year.

(a) a VAT invoice dated 9 July is sent out on 9 July for services supplied on 9 July

(b) a VAT invoice dated 9 July is sent out on 10 July for services supplied on 6 July

(c) a VAT invoice dated 9 July is issued on 9 July for goods supplied on 30 June

(d) a VAT invoice dated 31 July is issued on 1 August for services supplied on 7 July

(e) a pro-forma invoice dated 31 July is issued on 31 July for goods ordered on 28 July

14.5 On the next three pages are examples of sales invoices issued by VAT registered businesses.

Are they valid VAT invoices? If not, why not?

SALES INVOICE

Keeping Sweet

Confectioners

29 Mintfield Street, Broadfield, BR7 4ER
Tel 01908 887634 Fax 01908 887239 Email sugarplum@sweet.goblin.com

Delia's Deli
36 The Arcade
Broadfield
BR1 4GH

invoice no	893823
account	3945
your reference	SP84
date/tax point	21 04 99

deliver to

as above

details	quantity	price	amount (excl VAT)	VAT rate %	VAT amount £
Cheesecake – summerfruit	20	5.50	110.00		19.25
Raspberry Pavlova	30	6.25	187.50		32.81

terms
Net monthly
Carriage paid
E & OE

Total (excl VAT)	297.50
VAT	52.06
TOTAL	349.56

SALES INVOICE

Trend Designs

Unit 40 Elgar Estate, Broadfield, BR7 4ER
Tel 01908 765365 Fax 01908 7659507 Email lisa@trend.u-net.com
VAT Reg GB 0745 4172 20

invoice to

```
'Tone Up' Sports Shop
38 The Arcade
Broadfield
BR1 4GH
```

invoice no	788776
account	4013
your reference	2067
date/tax point	21 05 99

deliver to

```
as above
```

details	quantity	price	amount (excl VAT)	VAT rate %	VAT amount £
'Surf Dood' T-shirts	20	5.50	110.00	17.5	19.25
'Surf Baby' tracksuits	15	15.50	232.50	17.5	40.69

terms
Net monthly
Carriage paid
E & OE

Total (excl VAT)	342.50
VAT	59.94
TOTAL	402.44

SALES INVOICE

Champ Cleaners
17 High Street, Broadfield, BR7 4ER
Tel 01908 283472 Fax 01908 283488

invoice to

Premier Insurance
49 Farrier Street
Broadfield
BR1 4LY

invoice no	787906
account	3993
your reference	1956

details	price
Office Cleaning 16 hrs	104.00

Total (excl VAT)	
VAT	
TOTAL	122.20

14.6 You work in the accounts office of a building firm. A trainee working on Purchase Ledger brings to your attention a number of low value invoices received from T Walker Joinery (which is registered for VAT). These invoices do not have the VAT amount specified – just the overall total. They *do* show the name and address of the supplier, the VAT registration number, the date of supply, the details of the goods and the VAT rate. The amounts are:

1   £18.21

2   £64.62

3   £94.00

4   £1.76

5   £93.94

6   £23.50

The trainee says "These are not valid VAT invoices – how are we supposed to enter them in the day book? There is no VAT amount shown."

You are to:

(a)   State whether the invoices are valid invoices, and if they are, why they are.

(b)   Show the trainee how to work out the VAT and the net amount by carrying out the appropriate calculation for all six invoices.

14.7 You work in the accounts department of a VAT-registered stationery supply business. You are asked to issue a pro-forma invoice to a customer who wishes to place an order but has not dealt with your firm before.

You have been asked by your supervisor to telephone the customer and to explain:

(a)   when the goods will be despatched

(b)   what a pro-forma invoice is

(c)   the VAT implications of a pro-forma invoice (the customer is also VAT-registered)

Write down in numbered points what you would say to the customer.

Note: if time permits this Activity could alternatively be carried out orally between student and tutor.

14.8 You work for a firm of accountants and are asked to advise a client, Jim Tredwell, who is planning to start an import/export agency for carpets and rugs. He has a number of questions:

(a)   "If I import rugs from India, do I have to pay tax to HM Customs & Excise? What rate would apply?"

(b)   "If I export a UK-manufactured Axminster carpet to a client in Oman, do I have to charge him VAT?"

(c)   "If I import a nylon/wool mix carpet from Belgium, do I have to pay tax to HM Customs & Excise? What rate would apply?"

(d)   "I have a client in Germany who is interested in high quality Wilton carpets. Do I have to charge her VAT?"

You are to state what your answer would be in each case. Ensure that you mention any difference made by VAT registration by the buyer or seller. Mr Tredwell is likely to have to register for VAT when he starts trading.

15 VAT RECORDS AND THE VAT RETURN

15.1 You work for Simpson & Co, Accountants, and have been given the VAT figures from the accounts of four clients.

You are to draw up a VAT control account for each client company to calculate the VAT due or reclaimable for the VAT period. You can use the format shown at the bottom of the page. If the final total is reclaimable VAT, it should be shown in brackets.

VAT FIGURES	Homer Ltd	Bart Ltd	Marge Ltd	Lisa Ltd
	£	£	£	£
Purchases Day Book	3,120.00	2,739.50	7,826.65	2,713.50
Sales Day Book	6,461.70	4,806.33	10,632.40	985.67
Credit notes received	530.50	231.60	987.60	156.70
Credit notes issued	245.79	542.77	876.34	87.23
Cash book purchases (non-credit)	567.90	765.91	145.78	978.67
Cash book sales (non-credit)	461.75	1,675.80	1,287.89	568.23
Petty cash book purchases	15.95	21.67	45.78	24.55
EU Acquisitions	796.30	nil	4,875.89	nil
VAT overpaid previous period	nil	345.78	654.89	78.60
VAT underpaid previous period	34.87	nil	637.98	nil
Bad debt relief	156.67	476.50	nil	65.50

VAT deductible (input tax)	VAT payable (output tax)
Purchases Day Book VAT total, *less* any credit notes received	Sales Day Book VAT total, *less* any sales credit notes issued
Cash Book – items not in Purchases Day Book	Cash Book – items not in Sales Day Book
Petty Cash Book – VAT on small expenses	
Acquisitions from EU states	Acquisitions from EU states
Corrections of errors from previous periods (not exceeding £2,000 net)	Corrections of errors from previous periods (not exceeding £2,000 net)
Bad debt relief	
= TOTAL TAX DEDUCTIBLE	= TOTAL TAX PAYABLE
	less TOTAL TAX DEDUCTIBLE
	equals TAX PAYABLE/(RECLAIMABLE)

15.2 In your work for Simpson & Co you have been asked to sort out the VAT Return of Damon Driver, a local businessman who has set up a computer equipment firm in the town. He has presented you with two box files of invoices, one marked 'Purchases/expenses' and the other marked 'Sales'. He says he has been 'so busy' that he hasn't had time to sort them out. You make a list of the invoices as follows:

PURCHASES/EXPENSES				SALES			
Supplier	net £	VAT £	gross £	Customer	net £	VAT £	gross £
Amax Machines	234.56	41.04	275.60	B Keaton	56.00	9.80	65.80
Electra Limited	5,467.80	956.86	6,424.66	C Chaplin	678.00	118.65	796.65
Microhard PLC	9,567.90	1,674.38	11,242.28	Laurel College	45,786.90	8,012.70	53,799.60
Peach Computers	5,278.89	923.80	6,202.69	Hardy & Co	17,678.50	3,093.73	20,772.23
Elsa Products	560.00	98.00	658.00	A Sim	1,250.00	218.75	1,468.75
IPM Computers	19,780.00	3,461.50	23,241.50	T Thomas	16,900.00	2,957.50	19,857.50
				E Sykes Ltd	12,500.00	2,187.50	14,687.50
				H Jacques	3,467.80	606.86	4,074.66
				V Singh	450.00	78.75	528.75
				L San	400.00	70.00	470.00
				A Larsen	125.00	21.87	146.87
				Z Zidane	780.50	136.58	917.08
				M Santos	56.00	9.80	65.80

Damon tells you that these are all the credit transactions for the quarter. He also mentions:

• he has made cash sales of £940 (including VAT) and incurred petty cash expenses of £76.37 (including VAT)

• there were no EU acquisitions, corrections, bad debts, or credit notes issued or received

You are to:

(a) total the money columns of the invoice listings in the above table

(b) construct a VAT control account (see the previous page for the format)

(c) state what figures you would transfer to the VAT 100 by completing the schedule below

VAT due on sales and other outputs	
VAT reclaimed on purchases	
VAT due/reclaimable	
Total value of sales and other outputs (excluding VAT)	
Total value of purchases and other inputs (excluding VAT)	

15.3 Julie Roberts is managing director of Pretty Woman Limited, a company which manufactures cosmetic accessories. The business is VAT-registered and submits its VAT Return quarterly at the end of March, June, September and December.

The business address is Unit 17 Everbeech Estate, Newtown, NW3 5TG. The VAT Registration number is 454 7106 51.

You work in the accounts department of Pretty Woman Limited and have been given the task of completing the VAT Return for the quarter ending 31 December of the current year.

You have collected the following data from the manual accounting records.

SALES DAY BOOK SUMMARY

	standard-rated sales	VAT	total sales
	£	£	£
October	2,567.89	449.38	3,017.27
November	2,675.90	468.28	3,144.18
December	3,456.89	604.95	4,061.84

PURCHASES DAY BOOK SUMMARY

	standard-rated purchases	VAT	total purchases
	£	£	£
October	1,456.90	254.95	1,711.85
November	3,456.20	604.83	4,061.03
December	1,490.25	260.79	1,751.04

CASH BOOK & PETTY CASH BOOK – NON CREDIT ITEMS (October - December)

	net	VAT	total
	£	£	£
Cash sales	1,245.67	217.99	1,463.66
Petty cash expenses	67.80	11.86	79.66

ADDITIONAL INFORMATION

- Acquisitions from the EU for the period amounted to £850.70 net (VAT due of £148.87).

- Sales credit notes issued during the quarter amount to £345.70 + £60.49 VAT = £406.19.

- Credit notes received from suppliers amount to £400.00 + £70.00 VAT = £470.00.

- Bad debts written off during the year are:

    - £528.75 (invoice due 15 March, goods supplied 14 February)

    - £693.21 (invoice due 20 August, goods supplied 20 July)

    These invoice totals include VAT.

- In the previous VAT quarter there were two small errors in the accounts: output (sales) tax was underpaid by £44.50 and input tax (purchases) was over-estimated by £55.50.

You are to:

(a) Complete the VAT Control Account (format shown below) for the October - December quarter.

(b) Complete the VAT 100 form shown on the next page, ready for Julie Roberts' signature. Note that the year is shown as 'XX'; in reality the year would be shown as two digits.

VAT control account			
VAT deductible: input tax	£	**VAT payable: output tax**	£
Purchases Day Book		Sales Day Book	
less credit notes		*less* credit notes	
Cash Book		Cash Book	
Petty Cash Book			
EU Acquisitions		EU Acquisitions	
Correction of error		Correction of error	
Bad debt relief			
TOTAL INPUT TAX		TOTAL OUTPUT TAX	
		less TOTAL INPUT TAX	
		equals VAT DUE	

SPECIMEN

HM Customs and Excise

For the period
01 10 XX to 31 12 XX

625 454 7108 51 100 03 99 Q25147

PRETTY WOMAN LIMITED
17 EVERBEECH ESTATE
NEWTOWN
NW3 5TG

Your VAT Office telephone number is 01905 855600

Registration Number	Period
454 7108 51	12 XX

You could be liable to a financial penalty if your completed return and all the VAT payable are not received by the due date.

Due date: 31 01 XX

For
Official
Use

Before you fill in this form please read the notes on the back and the VAT leaflet *"Filling in your VAT return"*. Fill in all boxes in ink, and write 'none' where necessary. Don't put a dash or leave any box blank. If there are no pence write "00" in the pence column **Do not** enter more than one amount in any box.

For official use			£	p
	VAT due in this period on **sales** and other outputs	**1**		
	VAT due in this period on **acquisitions** from other **EC Member States**	**2**		
	Total VAT due **(the sum of boxes 1 and 2)**	**3**		
	VAT reclaimed in this period on **purchases** and other inputs (including acquisitions from the EC)	**4**		
	Net VAT to be paid to Customs or reclaimed by you **(Difference between boxes 3 and 4)**	**5**		
	Total value of **sales** and all other outputs excluding any VAT. **Include your box 8 figure**	**6**		00
	Total value of **purchases** and all other inputs excluding any VAT. **Include your box 9 figure**	**7**		00
	Total value of all **supplies** of goods and related services, excluding any VAT, to other **EC Member States**	**8**		00
	Total value of all **acquisitions** of goods and related services, excluding any VAT, from other **EC Member States**	**9**		00

Retail schemes. If you have used any of the schemes in the period covered by this return, enter the relevant letter(s) in this box.

DECLARATION: You, or someone on your behalf, must sign below.

I, ...declare that the
(Full name of signatory in BLOCK LETTERS)

information given above is true and complete.

Signature ....Date ....19.............

A false declaration can result in prosecution.

If you are enclosing a payment please tick this box.

L

Reports & Returns Assignments

ASSIGNMENTS

1   Mixed Retailers plc

2   City Hotels Limited

3   Thorington and Seaforth mines

This section contains three assignments to help students prepare for assessment for elements 1 and 2 of Unit 6 'Preparing Reports and Returns'.

The activities in these assignments are reproduced by kind permission of AAT.

ASSIGNMENT
MIXED RETAILERS PLC

1

SECTION 1

This assignment is in two sections.

You are advised to spend approximately one hour on this section.

DATA

You are an accounting technician employed by Mixed Retailers plc, which owns a large number of stores selling a wide variety of products throughout the UK. Mixed Retailers plc is currently investigating the performance of a number of companies retailing electrical goods with a view to purchasing a chain of stores in that sector of the market.

As an accounting technician in the accounting department of Mixed Retailers plc you have been asked by the chief accountant to carry out a number of analyses of the accounts of two companies retailing electrical goods.

Task 1.1

You have obtained data for the last two years for two companies – Alpha and Beta.

Analyse the data by completing the table on the next page.

Show the average size of store and sales per employee to the nearest whole number.

Show net profit/sales as a percentage to two decimal places.

PERFORMANCE DATA

	Company Alpha		Company Beta	
Year	1998	1999	1998	1999
Number of stores	281	279	226	231
Total area (sq m)	1,110,000	1,200,000	191,000	180,000
Number of employees	14,700	16,200	5,050	5,100
Sales (£m)	1,050	1,350	495	510
Net profit (£m)	51.1	52.0	15.7	16.8
Sales per sq m (£)	946	1,125	2,592	2,833
Average size of store (sq m)				
Net profit/sales (%)				
Sales per employee (£)				

Task 1.2

Prepare a report for the chief accountant comparing the performance of Alpha and Beta, using your own stationery.

Your report should be well-presented and address the following issues:

- size
- profitability
- efficiency

Your report should conclude by presenting the key differences in performance between the two companies. You should not attempt to make recommendations.

SECTION 2

You are advised to spend approximately one hour on this section.

As well as Alpha and Beta, Mixed Retailers plc is thinking of purchasing a third company, Gamma. The chief accountant of Mixed Retailers plc is concerned about some comments made in the annual report of Gamma. In this report the managing director of Gamma makes the following statement:

'Although sales have increased each year from 1995 to 1999, operating profits took a slight dip in 1997 and 1998 before rising to record levels in 1999.'

Relevant figures from the report are as follows:

	1995	1996	1997	1998	1999
Sales (£m)	3003.6	3235.4	3288.8	3547.9	4479.4
Operating profit (£m)	237.6	240.5	218.9	208.7	318.2
% Change in Operating Profit	–	1.22%	- 8.98%	- 4.66%	52.47%
Operating profit as % of sales	7.91%	7.43%	6.66%	5.88%	7.10%
Sales at 1999 prices (£m)					
Operating profit at 1999 prices (£m)	269.5	264.1	231.1	214.2	318.2
UK Retail Price Index	133.3	137.7	143.2	147.3	151.2

Task 2.1

Complete the table above by calculating sales for each year at 1999 prices. Your figures should be shown as £m rounded to one decimal place.

Task 2.2

Prepare a line graph, using the graph paper on the next page, showing the trend in sales and operating profit at 1999 prices from 1995 to 1999.

Note: a bar chart will not be acceptable.

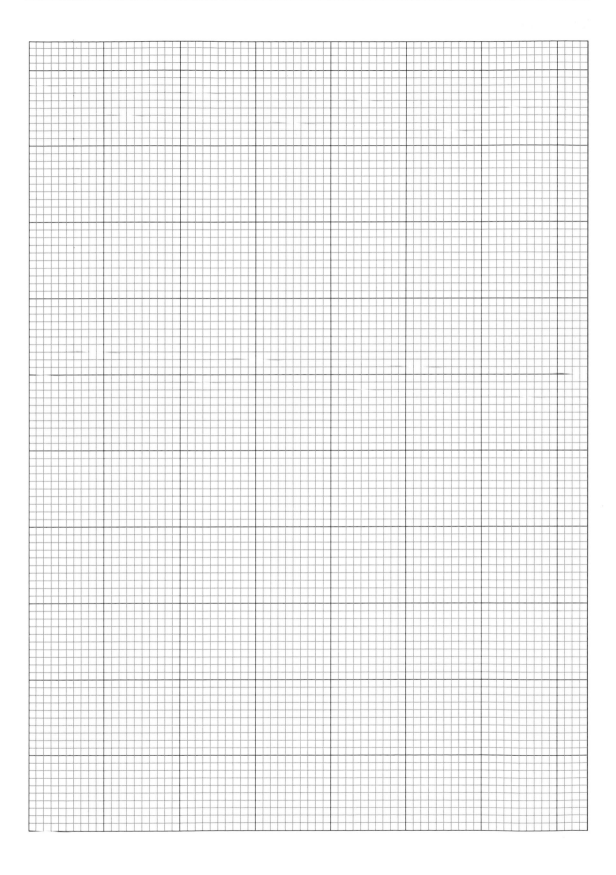

Task 2.3

Write a memo using the stationery shown below, stating whether you agree or disagree with the statement made by the managing director of Gamma. Support your conclusions with evidence, using the data on page 66 and your answers to Tasks 2.1 and 2.2.

MEMO

TO:

FROM:

DATE:

SUBJECT:

ASSIGNMENT
CITY HOTELS LIMITED

2

SECTION 1

This assignment is in two sections.

You are advised to spend approximately 1 hour 20 minutes on this section.

DATA

You are an accounting technician working for City Hotels Limited, which owns three hotels in London.

- The Station Hotel is situated near a main railway station and its customers are mainly railway travellers, business people and weekend visitors.

- The Airport Hotel is situated near the airport and its customers are virtually all air travellers who stay in the hotel either before or after their flight.

- The Central Hotel is situated in the city centre and is used mainly by tourists, business people and weekend visitors.

City Hotels Limited wishes to compare the performances of the three hotels and has asked you to carry out a series of analyses to enable this to be done.

Basic Data

	Station Hotel	Airport Hotel	Central Hotel
Number of Rooms	140	210	90
Standard Room Tariff	£42.00	£45.00	£60.00

Notes:

- Each hotel has only double rooms. The standard room tariff is the price of a double room per night.

- City Hotels Limited runs a variety of discount schemes and special offers whereby rooms can be obtained at cheaper rates.

City Hotels Limited

Performance Statistics for the week ended 31 May 1999

	Sun	Mon	Tues	Wed	Thurs	Fri	Sat
Station Hotel:							
No. of Rooms Let	80	110	108	106	105	96	121
Total Room Revenue	£2,856	£4,316	£4,312	£4,324	£4,221	£3,614	£3,460
Room Occupancy Rate	57%	79%	77%	76%	75%	69%	86%
Average Rate per Room Let	£35.70	£39.24	£39.93	£40.79	£40.20	£37.65	£28.60
Airport Hotel:							
No. of Rooms Let	182	192	186	174	195	184	173
Total Room Revenue	£8,074	£8,460	£8,241	£7,542	£8,418	£7,840	£7,518
Room Occupancy Rate	87%	91%	89%	83%	93%	88%	82%
Average Rate per Room Let	£44.36	£44.06	£44.31	£43.34	£43.17	£42.61	£43.46
Central Hotel:							
No. of Rooms Let	64	68	69	46	52	65	82
Total Room Revenue	£3,440	£3,652	£3,541	£2,416	£2,867	£3,216	£3,962
Room Occupancy Rate	71%	76%	77%	51%	58%	72%	91%
Average Rate per Room Let	£53.75	£53.71	£51.32	£52.52	£55.13	£49.48	£48.32

Task 1.1

Complete the Summary Performance Statistics below for City Hotels Limited.

City Hotels Limited

Summary Performance Statistics for the week ended 31 May 1999

	Station Hotel	Airport Hotel	Central Hotel
Total Rooms Let			
Average Room Occupancy Rate			
Total Room Revenue			
Average Rate per Room Let			

Note: Average room occupancy rate is to be shown to the nearest whole percentage. The average rate per room let is to be shown to the nearest penny.

Task 1.2

Prepare a report for City Hotels Limited, comparing the performances of the three hotels for the week ending 31 May 1999. Use the information on pages 69 to 71, including the statistics prepared by you in Task 1.1.

Your report should address the following issues:

- room occupancy rates;

- rates per room let;

- possible recommendations for the future, giving evidence for your reasoning;

- any limitations in the data provided.

Use your own stationery for the report.

SECTION 2

You are advised to spend approximately 40 minutes on this section.

The hotel accountant has asked you to compare the performance of the three hotels in terms of the revenue from rooms let, over the last five years.

DATA

City Hotels Limited

Revenue from Rooms Let 1994 - 1998

	1994	1995	1996	1997	1998
Station Hotel	£1,150,000	£1,250,000	£1,200,000	£1,250,000	£1,300,000
Airport Hotel	£1,250,000	£1,400,000	£2,300,000	£2,600,000	£2,750,000
Central Hotel	£850,000	£900,000	£850,000	£950,000	£1,100,000

Task 2.1

Using the graph paper on the next page, prepare a clearly labelled line graph showing the performance of the three hotels for the period 1994-1998.

Note: a bar chart will *not* be acceptable.

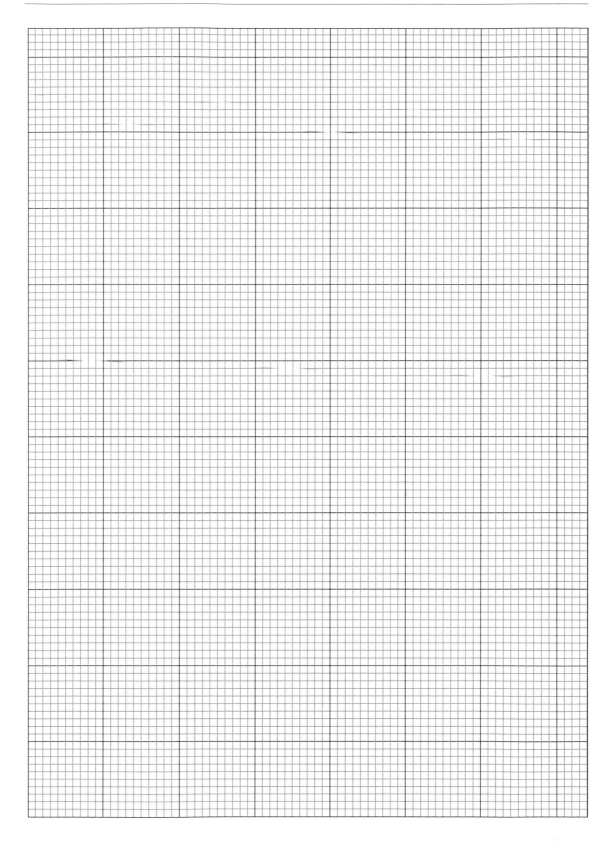

Task 2.2

Prepare a memorandum for the hotel accountant on the form shown below. The memorandum should:

- analyse the trends revealed by the graph prepared in Task 2.1
- highlight any limitations in trends revealed by your analysis

MEMORANDUM

TO:

FROM:

DATE:

SUBJECT:

ASSIGNMENT
THORINGTON AND SEAFORTH MINES

3

SECTION 1

This assignment is in two sections.

You are advised to spend approximately 1 hour 30 minutes on this section.

DATA

You are an accounting technician working for a company that specialises in consultancy to the coal mining industry. Your company has been approached by a small coal mining company that has two mines:

(1)   an underground deep mine in the north of the country at Thorington

(2)   a surface open-cast mine in the south of the country at Seaforth

The output from the underground coal mine at Thorington is mainly for home consumption, whilst the output from the open-cast coal mine at Seaforth is primarily for export. The home market for coal is under threat from competition from cheaper overseas coal and home produced natural gas, whilst the overseas market is more traditional and there is a steady demand.

The coal mining company wants to develop a third mine and is unsure whether it should be a deep or open-cast mine. The third mine would be in the locality of one of its two existing mines. The coal mining company has carried out the prospecting and exploration stages near to the location of its current mines and is now ready to proceed to the development and exploitation stages at the chosen site. Work to date has shown that yields and costs for both potential mines would be similar to the yields and costs of the existing mines in the locality as shown on the next page.

The data on the next page relates to the performance of the Thorington underground mine and the Seaforth open-cast surface mine over the last three years.

PERFORMANCE DATA

	1997	1998	1999
Tonnes of coal excavated (000s)			
Thorington	471.6	472.2	472.9
Seaforth	293.6	315.2	341.7
Number of employees			
Thorington	237	244	253
Seaforth	162	164	170
Excavation costs (£000s)			
Thorington	13,456	13,892	13,999
Seaforth	9,117	9,135	9,189
Net profit (£000s)			
Thorington	6,943	6,995	7,083
Seaforth	4,437	4,839	5,173

Task 1.1

You are given the following table of performance statistics. Complete the table for the Seaforth coal mine.

PERFORMANCE STATISTICS

THORINGTON UNDERGROUND DEEP MINE 1997-99

	1997	1998	1999
Coal extracted per employee (tonnes)	1,990	1,935	1,869
Excavation costs per tonne of coal excavated (£)	28.54	29.42	29.60
Net profit per tonne of coal excavated (£)	14.72	14.81	14.98
Net profit per employee (£000)	29.30	28.67	28.00

SEAFORTH OPEN-CAST MINE 1997-99

	1997	1998	1999
Coal extracted per employee (tonnes)			
Excavation costs per tonne of coal excavated (£)			
Net profit per tonne of coal excavated (£)			
Net profit per employee (£000)			

Note: Show figures to the same number of decimal places as for the Thorington mine.

SECTION 2

You are advised to spend approximately 30 minutes on this section.

DATA

The finance director has asked you to review the coal excavated per employee at the Thorington and Seaforth mines against the industry average for 1997-1999.

	Coal excavated per employee Industry Average (tonnes)
1997	1,890
1998	1,920
1999	1,940

Task 2.1

(a)   Using the graph paper on the next page, prepare a clearly labelled line graph showing the performance of the Thorington and Seaforth mines against the industry performance for the period 1997 to 1999.

(b)   Prepare a memorandum for the finance director using the stationery on page 80 analysing the trends revealed by the graph you have prepared in Task 2.1 (a) for the period 1997 to 1999.

Task 2.2

Prepare a report for your finance director (using your own stationery) comparing the performance of the Thorington and Seaforth mines. Your report should address the following issues using your results from Task 1.1 and the information available on pages 76 to 78:

- profitability

- efficiency

- future outlook

You should advise your finance director which potential mine should be taken forward to the development and exploitation stages by the mining company on the basis of the data available for the two present mines.

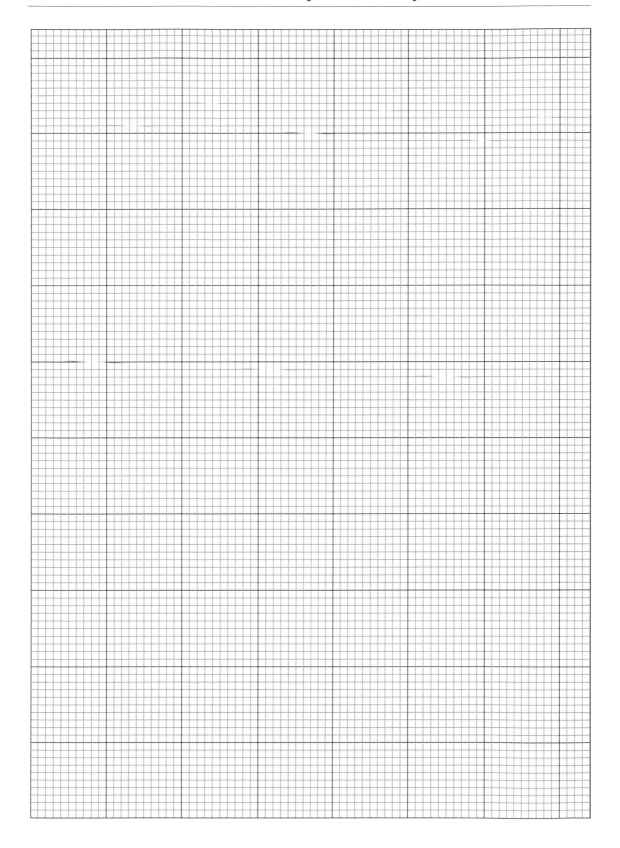

MEMORANDUM

TO:

FROM:

DATE:

SUBJECT:

Costing Simulation 1

Polycot Limited

reproduced by kind permission of AAT

suggested time limit 4 hours

SCENARIO

This simulation is based on Polycot Limited, a company which manufactures cotton duvet covers. The tasks include:

- completion of stores record cards
- analysis of wages and entry into cost ledger data entry sheet
- assessment of overhead absorption
- calculation of overhead absorption rates
- completion of a standard cost card
- analysis of variances

NVQ UNIT 5 – ELEMENTS COVERED

1   record and analyse information relating to direct costs

2   record and analyse information relating to the allocation, apportionment and absorption of overhead costs

3   prepare and present standard cost reports

SIMULATION POLYCOT LIMITED

THE SITUATION

Your name is Lesley Hunt and you work as an accounts assistant for Polycot Limited, a manufacturer of cotton duvet covers.

COST CENTRES

The production cost centres in Polycot Limited are a cutting department, a finishing department and a packing department.

- Work in the cutting department is machine-intensive. The machines are operated by a number of direct employees.

- Work in the finishing department and packing departments is labour-intensive, and is carried out entirely by direct employees of Polycot Limited.

In addition to the production cost centres there is also a stores department.

COST ACCOUNTING RECORDS

Polycot Limited uses the FIFO method of valuing issues of materials to production and stocks of materials. The company is registered for VAT and all of its outputs are standard-rated. This means that VAT on its purchases can always be reclaimed and should therefore be ignored in the cost records.

The accounts code list for the company includes the following codes:

Cost centre codes		Expenditure codes	
C100	Cutting department	E200	Direct materials
C200	Finishing department	E210	Indirect materials
C300	Packing department	E300	Direct wages
C400	Stores	E310	Indirect wages
		E410	Indirect revenue expenses
		E500	Depreciation - production equipment

Until now, the company has absorbed all production overheads on the basis of a percentage of direct labour costs. However, as you will see, a change is proposed in this area for the coming year. Whatever method of overhead absorption is used, any under or over absorption is transferred to the profit and loss account at the end of each quarter.

PERSONNEL

The personnel involved in the simulation are as follows:

Production manager   Jim Stubbs

General manager   Patrick McGrath

In the simulation you will begin by dealing with certain transactions in the month of March 1998, and you will then be involved in forecasting outcomes for the company's financial year ending 31 March 1999. Finally, you will use your results to account for transactions in July 1998. Note that for many of the tasks you will need to prepare rough workings; you should use your own stationery for this purpose.

THE TASKS TO BE PERFORMED

PART 1: TRANSACTIONS IN MARCH 1998 (pages 85 to 97)

1   Refer to the purchase invoices and materials requisitions on pages 85 to 89. Using this information you are required to complete the stores ledger account cards for the month of March 1998 on pages 90 and 91. You are reminded that the company uses the FIFO method. You may assume that suppliers raise invoices on the same day that goods are delivered.

2   You are required to prepare a memo for the general manager, Patrick McGrath, drawing attention to any unusual matters concerning stock levels of the items dealt with in Task 1 above. Use the blank memo form on page 92 and date the document 3 April 1998.

3   Time sheets for two employees of Polycot Limited are shown on pages 94 and 95. These employees work on the production of duvet covers. Using the information contained in the internal policy document on page 93, you are required to analyse their wages for the week ending 6 March 1998, as follows:

   •   Complete the total column in each timesheet.

   •   Check for discrepancies and make any necessary adjustments.

   •   Calculate the bonus earned by each employee on each day and in total for the week, and enter the appropriate amounts on the timesheets.

   •   Complete the analysis at the bottom of each timesheet.

   •   Enter the appropriate figures on the cost ledger data entry sheet on page 96.

4   Prepare a memo to the production manager, Jim Stubbs, outlining any discrepancies in the wages data for these two employees for the week and requesting assistance in resolving your queries. Use the blank memo form on page 97 and date the document 10 March 1998.

PART 2: OVERHEAD ABSORPTION FOR 1998/99 (pages 98 to 103)

5   The company at present absorbs all production overheads as a percentage of direct labour costs. The company is considering a revision in this policy for the accounting year 1998/99. Under the proposed new policy, a machine hour rate would be used in the cutting department, and direct labour hour rates in the finishing and packing departments. You are required to write a memo to the production manager, Jim Stubbs, explaining why the proposal is appropriate. Use the blank form on page 99 and date the document 10 March 1998.

6   Refer to the information given on page 98. Using this information, you are required to calculate 1998/99 overhead absorption rates for each production department: cutting (machine hour rate), finishing (direct labour hour rate) and packing (direct labour hour rate). Use the analysis sheet on page 100 for your calculations.

7   Refer to the memo on page 101. You are required to use the information in this memo to perform the following tasks:

(a)   Write a memo to the production manager, Jim Stubbs, concerning the query on the wages for the temporary employee. Explain precisely and clearly what information you would need to be able to fully analyse and classify the hours worked by the employee and the wages paid. Use the blank memo form on page 102 and date the document 6 July 1998.

For the remainder of the task, you are required to ignore the pending query concerning the temporary employee.

(b)   Using the overhead absorption rate that you calculated in task 6 and the information contained in the labour hours analysis, calculate the production overhead absorbed in the Packing department during the quarter ending 30 June 1998. Insert your result in the working sheet at the top of page 103.

(c)   Using the information on the costs charged to cost centre code C300, determine the total actual production overhead cost for the packing department for the quarter ending 30 June 1998. Insert your result in the working sheet at the top of page 103.

(d)   Determine the amount to be transferred to the profit and loss account for the quarter ending 30 June 1998 in respect of under or over absorbed production overheads for the packing department. Indicate clearly whether the overheads are under or over absorbed for the quarter. Insert your result in the working sheet at the top of page 103.

PART 3: STANDARD COSTS AND VARIANCES, JULY 1998 (pages 103 to 106)

8   Refer to the information on page 103. Using this information you are required to complete the standard cost card on page 104. Note that you may need to refer to the following information: your completed stores ledger cards on pages 90 and 91; the direct labour hour rate on page 93 and the overhead absorption rates that you calculated in task 6.

9   Refer to the memo on page 105. You are required to prepare a memo, addressed to the general manager, Patrick McGrath, analysing all of the variances arising during the week ended 8 July 1998 and suggesting possible reasons for the main variances. You should date your report 13 July 1998. Use the memo form on page 106.

Note: in addition to the information referred to above, you will also need to refer to the overhead absorption rates that you calculated in task 6 and the standard cost card that you prepared in task 8.

SALES INVOICE

KENILWORTH LIMITED
12 Luton Road, Mapleton, Bedfordshire LU4 8EN
Telephone: 01582 622411

VAT registration: 291 8753 42

Date/tax point: 2 March 1998

Invoice to:
Polycot Limited
17 Hightown Road
Branston
BN4 3EW

Invoice number: 2078

Your order: 3901

Item description	Quantity	Unit price £	Trade discount @ 30% £	Net price £	Total £
Plastic poppers (100 in each box)	100 boxes	91.00	27.30	63.70	6,370.00
Total					6,370.00
VAT at 17.5%					1,114.75
Total due					7,484.75

Terms: net 30 days

SALES INVOICE

BAXTER LIMITED
39 Langdale Avenue, Bisham MW3 9TY
Telephone: 01693 77612

VAT registration: 215 8761 34

Date/tax point: 6 March 1998

Invoice to:
Polycot Limited
17 Hightown Road
Branston
BN4 3EW

Invoice number: 7123

Your order: 3889

Item description	Quantity	Unit price £	Trade discount @ 30% £	Net price £	Total £
Cotton—50 metre rolls	90	124.00	37.20	86.80	7,812.00
Total					7,812.00
VAT at 17.5%					1,367.10
Total due					9,179.10

Terms: net 30 days

SALES INVOICE

KENILWORTH LIMITED
12 Luton Road, Mapleton, Bedfordshire LU4 8EN
Telephone: 01582 622411

VAT registration: 291 8753 42

Date/tax point: 9 March 1998

Invoice to:
Polycot Limited
17 Hightown Road
Branston
BN4 3EW

Invoice number: 2115

Your order: 3912

Item description	Quantity	Unit price £	Trade discount @ 30% £	Net price £	Total £
Plastic poppers (100 in each box)	100 boxes	92.00	27.60	64.40	6,440.00
Total VAT at 17.5%					6,440.00 1,127.00
Total due					7,567.00
Terms: net 30 days					

SALES INVOICE

Hartston Limited
55 Parlour Street, Jamestown, FE6 8UR
Telephone: 01225 67124

VAT registration: 214 5143 28

Date/tax point: 12 March 1998

Invoice to:
Polycot Limited
17 Hightown Road
Branston
BN4 3EW

Invoice number: 34415

Your order: 3932

Item description	Quantity	Unit price £	Trade discount @ 30% £	Net price £	Total £
Plastic poppers (100 in each box)	100 boxes	95.00	28.50	66.50	6,650.00
Total VAT at 17.5%					6,650.00 1,163.75
Total due					7,813.75
Terms: net 30 days					

SALES INVOICE

BAXTER LIMITED
39 Langdale Avenue, Bisham MW3 9TY
Telephone: 01693 77612

VAT registration: 215 8761 34

Date/tax point: 12 March 1998

Invoice to:
Polycot Limited
17 Hightown Road
Branston
BN4 3EW

Invoice number: 7249

Your order: 3917

Item description	Quantity	Unit price £	Trade discount @ 30% £	Net price £	Total £
Cotton—50 metre rolls	90	126.00	37.80	88.20	7,938.00
Total					7,938.00
VAT at 17.5%					1,389.15
Total due					9,327.15

Terms: net 30 days

MATERIALS REQUISITION

DATE	6 March 1998	NUMBER	944

DEPARTMENT   Finishing

QUANTITY	CODE	DESCRIPTION
90	PP29	Plastic poppers

SIGNATURE   Jim Stubbs

MATERIALS REQUISITION

DATE	10 March 1998	NUMBER	948

DEPARTMENT   Cutting

QUANTITY	CODE	DESCRIPTION
50	CT33	Cotton, 50 metre rolls

SIGNATURE   Jim Stubbs

MATERIALS REQUISITION

DATE	18 March 1998	NUMBER	959

DEPARTMENT   Cutting

QUANTITY	CODE	DESCRIPTION
40	CT33	Cotton, 50 metre rolls

SIGNATURE   Jim Stubbs

MATERIALS REQUISITION

DATE   20 March 1998   NUMBER   961

DEPARTMENT   Finishing

QUANTITY	CODE	DESCRIPTION
110	PP29	Plastic poppers

SIGNATURE   Jim Stubbs

MATERIALS REQUISITION

DATE   30 March 1998   NUMBER   984

DEPARTMENT   Cutting

QUANTITY	CODE	DESCRIPTION
30	CT33	Cotton, 50 metre rolls

SIGNATURE   Jim Stubbs

STORES LEDGER ACCOUNT

Material description: *Plastic poppers, boxes of 100*

Code no.: *PP29*

Maximum quantity: *180*
Minimum quantity: *62*
Reorder level: *95*
Reorder quantity: *100*

Date	Receipts			Issues			Stock balance		
	Quantity	Price £ per box	Total £	Quantity	Price £ per box	Total £	Quantity	Price £ per box	Total £
1 March							75	62.50	4,687.50

STORES LEDGER ACCOUNT

Material description: *Cotton, 50m rolls*

Code no.: *CT33*

Maximum quantity: *175*
Minimum quantity: *55*
Reorder level: *75*
Reorder quantity: *90*

Date	Receipts			Issues			Stock balance		
	Quantity	Price £ per roll	Total £	Quantity	Price £ per roll	Total £	Quantity	Price £ per roll	Total £
1 March							65	85.50	5,557.50

MEMORANDUM

To:

From:

Subject: **Date:**

INTERNAL POLICY DOCUMENT

Document no.   15

Subject: **Wages**

Issued: **December 1997**

Direct labour rates to be paid

Employee grade	£ per hour
1	4.00
2	3.00
3	2.50

The above rates are also payable for any hours spent on indirect work.

Direct employees work an eight hour day.

Overtime (any hours worked in excess of eight per day): employees are to be paid for one and a half hours for every hour of overtime that they work.

Employees will be paid a bonus of £0.15 for every duvet cover produced in excess of 60 in any single day. No in lieu bonuses are paid for idle time, training, etc.

Employees are to be credited with eight hours for any full days when they are sick, on holiday, or engaged in training activities. Half or part days are credited on a pro rata basis. These hours are to be paid at the basic rate.

Analysis of wages

The following are to be treated as direct labour costs:

- Payment for hours spent on direct tasks
- The basic pay for overtime spent on direct tasks

The following are to be treated as indirect labour costs:

- Overtime premium payments
- Bonus payments
- Idle time payments
- Holiday pay, sick pay and training pay

Discrepancies on time sheets

The company wishes to facilitate the prompt payment of wages and early reporting of labour costs to management. Employees will initially be paid for the total number of hours shown at the bottom of their time sheet, plus appropriate bonuses and overtime premiums.

Any discrepancies on time sheets are to be temporarily adjusted within direct labour hours, pending the outcome of enquiries.

Timesheet   Week ending   *6 March 1998*

Employee name   *Amy Harding*   Employee number   *2173*

Department   *Finishing*   Employee grade   *2*

Activity	Monday	Tuesday	Wednesday	Thursday	Friday	Total
	Hours	Hours	Hours	Hours	Hours	Hours
Machining	7	10	4		4	
Holiday			4	8		
Waiting for work	1					
Training					4	
Total hours payable for day	8	10	8	8	8	
Number of covers produced	65	72	30	0	32	

Bonus payable @ £0.15 per
cover above 60 per day

Signed   *Amy Harding*   Manager   *Jim Stubbs*

- -

Analysis for week	Hours	Rate per hour £	Wages cost £
Direct wages			
Indirect wages			
Basic hours			
Overtime premium			
Bonus			

Timesheet Week ending   6 March 1998

Employee name   Jane Amber   Employee number   2487

Department   Cutting   Employee grade   1

Activity	**Monday** Hours	**Tuesday** Hours	**Wednesday** Hours	**Thursday** Hours	**Friday** Hours	**Total** Hours
Cutting	10	6	6		8	
Waiting for work		3	2			
Sick				8		
Training					2	
Total hours payable for day	10	8	8	8	10	
Number of covers produced	70	51	62	0	62	

Bonus payable @ £0.15 per
cover above 60 per day

Signed   Jane Amber   Manager   Jim Stubbs

- -

Analysis for week	Hours	Rate per hour £	Wages cost £
Direct wages			
Indirect wages			
Basic hours			
Overtime premium			
Bonus			
	____		____
	____		____

COST LEDGER DATA ENTRY SHEET

Week ending ....

Debit accounts

Cost centre code	Expenditure code	Amount to be debited £
C100	E300	
C200	E300	
C300	E300	
C400	E300	
C100	E310	
C200	E310	
C300	E310	
C400	E310	

Check total: total wages for the two employees

MEMORANDUM

To:

From:

Subject: **Date:**

PART 2

PRODUCTION OVERHEADS FOR THE YEAR TO 31 MARCH 1999

Polycot Limited rents its production premises. The rent and rates for the year to 31 March 1999 will amount to £79,500.

Catering facilities for production staff are limited to a number of vending machines dispensing drinks and snacks. The rent for these machines during the year ending 31 March 1999 will be £100 per month.

Machinery and equipment owned by Polycot is subject to a maintenance contract covering preventive and urgent maintenance, parts, labour and call out charges. For the year to 31 March 1999 the maintenance company will charge £25,250 in respect of the machinery in the cutting department, £5,600 in respect of machinery in the finishing department, £11,000 in respect of machinery in the packing department, and £4,000 in respect of machinery in the stores department. Depreciation on all machinery will total £13,490.

The production manager's salary will be £21,000 for the year; he divides his time equally between the three production departments. The storekeeper's salary will be £14,000.

Other production overheads for the year are estimated at £40,000. The general manager has suggested that this should be divided evenly across the four departments.

The following data is also available:

	Cutting	Finishing	Packing	Stores
Floor area (sq metres)	1,900	2,650	1,900	1,125
Number of employees	20	68	40	3
Cost of machinery	£74,125	£16,625	£32,300	£11,850
Direct labour hours	5,125	129,750	67,500	
Machine hours	30,750	28,350	10,750	
Number of materials requisitions	21,175	17,675	14,100	

MEMORANDUM

To:

From:

Subject: **Date:**

OVERHEAD ANALYSIS SHEET: 1998/99

Overhead expense: primary apportionments and allocations	Basis of allocation/ apportionment	Total £	Cutting dept £	Finishing dept £	Packing dept £	Stores £

Total of primary allocations

Re-apportion stores

Total production cost centre overhead

Machine hours

Direct labour hours

Overhead absorption rate for 1998/99

MEMO

To: Lesley Hunt

From: Patrick McGrath, General Manager

Date: 3 July 1998

Subject: Overhead absorption, quarter ending 30 June 1998

Your colleague in the accounts department had almost completed the task of calculating the production overheads under or over absorbed for the last quarter. Unfortunately she was not able to complete the task before leaving for her summer holiday. She has asked me to pass on the following information, and assures me that you will know what to do in order to complete the calculations.

Thanks for your help.

Information attached to the memo:

Amounts charged to cost centre code C300 - Packing department: quarter ending 30 June 1998

Cost centre code	Expenditure code	Amount charged £
C300	E200	8,020
C300	E210	855
C300	E300	48,345
C300	E310	4,045
C300	E410	10,800
C300	E500	800

Labour hours analysis - quarter ending 30 June 1998

	Cutting department hours	Finishing department hours	Packing department hours
Direct labour hours	1,200	38,800	18,300
Indirect labour hours	890	1,250	1,830
Total labour hours	2,090	40,050	20,130

Note: the above tables do not include a payment that I still have to enquire about: wages of £1,920 were paid to a temporary employee for 320 hours worked during the quarter ending 30th June 1998.

MEMORANDUM

To:

From:

Subject: **Date:**

WORKING SHEET FOR CALCULATION OF OVERHEAD UNDER/OVER ABSORBED

Packing department, quarter ending 30 June 1998

7(b) Production overhead absorbed   £ ....

7(c) Actual production overhead incurred   £ ....

7(d) Production overhead under or over absorbed,
      to be transferred to profit and loss account   £ ....

PART 3

STANDARD COSTS FOR 1998/99

The General Manager, Patrick McGrath, has informed you of the following decisions relating to standard costs for double duvet covers for the year ending 31 March 1999.

Cotton prices

Assume a 5 per cent increase over the highest price paid in March 1998. (Refer back to the relevant stores ledger card for this information.)

Plastic poppers

Assume a price of £67 per box of 100.

Thread

Assume a price of £14.20 per 10,000 metres.

Packing cartons

Assume a price of £0.25 per box, each box being large enough for 6 double covers.

Direct labour

Assume a 5 per cent increase over current rates for all grades.

STANDARD COST CARD 1998/99

Product: Box of 6 double duvet covers
Product code no: 00214

Description	Material code no./ Direct labour grade	Quantity	Std. price £ per metre/ hour etc.	Total £
Direct materials				
Cotton fabric	CT33	38.2 metres		
Plastic poppers	PP29	60		
Polyester thread	TP72	22 metres		
Packing—cardboard box	PB03	1 box		
Other materials	Various	—	—	0.81
Subtotal, direct materials			(A)	
Direct labour				
Cutting	Grade 1	0.35 hours		
Finishing	Grade 1	4.10 hours		
Packing	Grade 3	0.50 hours		
Subtotal, direct labour			(B)	
Production overhead				
Cutting department		1.80 machine hours		
Finishing department		4.10 labour hours		
Packing department		0.50 labour hours		
Subtotal, production overhead			(C)	
Total standard production cost			(A + B + C)	

MEMORANDUM

To: Lesley Hunt

From: Patrick McGrath

Date: 12 July 1998

Subject: Standard cost report for double duvet covers in Cutting department

I have collated some of the data you will need for the standard cost report for week ended 8 July - see below.

Please could you let me have an analysis of all the cost variances that you can calculate from this, with explanations of any significant ones. I'd be grateful if you could let me have this by close of business tomorrow.

Cost data for week ended 8 July 1998 - double duvet covers in Cutting department

Output

Budgeted double covers produced in the week = 1,900

Actual double covers produced in the week = 1,760

Materials

Cotton used = 11,350 metres, costing £21,565

Direct labour

Cutting department = 90 hours of Grade 1 labour, costing £402

Machine hours

Cutting department = 560 machine hours

Overhead

Production overhead charged to Cutting department = £1,650

MEMORANDUM

To:

From:

Subject: **Date:**

Costing
Simulation 2

Boxit Limited

suggested time limit 4 hours

SCENARIO

This simulation is based on Boxit Limited, a company which manufactures metal
shelf units for use in offices. The tasks include:

- completion of stores ledger account
- analysis of wages and entry on a cost ledger data entry sheet
- an explanation of standard costing
- completion of overheads schedules
- completion of a standard cost card
- completion of a variance report

NVQ UNIT 5 – ELEMENTS COVERED

1   record and analyse information relating to direct costs

2   record and analyse information relating to the allocation, apportionment
    and absorption of overhead costs

3   prepare and present standard cost reports

SIMULATION BOXIT LIMITED

2

THE SITUATION

INTRODUCTION

Your name is John Raymond.

You have recently started work as an accounts assistant for Boxit Limited, a company which manufactures metal shelf units for use in offices. The administration of the firm is being reviewed and some changes are being considered. So that you may understand the present system and assist with the review, you are asked to complete various tasks.

You are reporting to Helen Jones, a senior in the accounts department.

You have the following information about the present system and further data for the tasks you are asked to carry out will be available on documents which you are given in the data section.

COST CENTRES

Boxit Limited is organised into three production cost centres: Construction, Painting and Packing. In all three production cost centres the work is carried out by direct employees of Boxit Limited. There are two service cost centres: Stores and Administration.

THE PRESENT COST ACCOUNTING SYSTEM

Boxit Limited uses the weighted average method of valuation for stocks and for issues of materials from stores to work in progress.

Sheet metal and metal frames are treated as direct materials, all other materials (eg paint, rivets, small fittings, packing materials) being treated as indirect.

Overheads are absorbed on the basis of direct labour hours, separate rates being calculated for each of the three production cost centres. Any over or under absorption of overheads is transferred to an Overhead Adjustment Account, from which the balance is transferred to the Profit and Loss Account at the end of the year. The financial year-end for Boxit Limited is 31 October.

VAT on purchases can be ignored in the costing records, as it can all be reclaimed.

The cost coding system for Boxit Limited includes the following codes:

Cost Centre Codes

CP10	Construction
CP20	Painting
CP30	Packing
CS40	Stores
CS50	Administration

Expenditure Codes

M100	Direct Materials
M200	Indirect Materials
W300	Direct Wages
W400	Indirect Wages

THE TASKS TO BE PERFORMED

1   Refer to the Memo dated 27 April 1998 from Helen Jones on page 110 and write a reply using the stationery on page 111.

2   Using the relevant documents from those relating to various materials on pages 112 to 114, complete the stores ledger account on page 115. You are reminded that the company uses the weighted average method of valuation. Assume that the supplier raises the invoice on the same day as delivery.

3   Using the documents relating to various materials on pages 112 to 114, complete the cost ledger data entry sheet on page 116.

4   Refer to the Memo from Helen Jones on page 117, dated 28 April 1998, and carry out the calculations requested. Reply to the Memo, answering all the questions, using the stationery on page 118.

5   Refer to the internal policy document on page 119 and the timesheets for three employees on page 120. Complete the calculation and analysis of gross wages for these employees on page 121. Read Task 6 below before commencing this task.

6   Using the stationery on page 122, write a Memo to Helen Jones, relating to any matters of uncertainty and assumptions you have had to make in Task 5 above.

7   Refer to the Memo from Helen Jones, dated 29 April 1998, on page 123 together with the attached notes on pages 123 to 124. Following the instructions given by Helen Jones, complete the schedules relating to overheads on page 125.

8   Using the stationery on page 126, write a Memo to Helen Jones stating whether you consider the revised methods of apportionment and absorption of overheads are an improvement on the previous system, giving brief reasons.

9   Using your answers to Task 7, for the revised system, complete the Standard Cost Card for a Shelf Unit on page 127. Some of the information has already been entered.

10   Refer to the Memo from Helen Jones, dated 30 April 1998, on page 128, and your answers to Task 4 and 7. Complete the Variance Report for the week ended 24 April 1998 at the bottom of page 128.

MEMORANDUM

To: John Raymond

From: Helen Jones

Date: 27 April 1998

Subject: Stock policies

As part of our review, we have been asked to look at stock policies and, to help with my report, I would like you to answer the following questions:

(1) One of our materials is a spray paint, used to finish the products. The demand for this paint is 7,500 litres per year (assume this is at a steady rate through 50 weeks). When it is ordered, the paint usually arrives 2 weeks later, but sometimes either 1 week or 3 weeks after an order is made. The cost of making an order is £10 and the cost of keeping one litre in stock for the year is £2.

   - What would you recommend as the Economic Order Quantity for the paint?

   - At what level should it be reordered?

   - What minimum and maximum control levels would you set for this item of stock?

(2) The Manager considers that it might be possible to use Just-in-Time stock control for our metal sheets and frames.

   - Can you explain briefly what this means?

   - What are the main advantages?

   - What are the main problems?

MEMORANDUM

To:

From:

Date:

Subject:

BALANCES EXTRACTED FROM STORES LEDGER

STOCK BALANCES AS AT 20 APRIL 1998

Code	Quantity	Unit Price	Total
108	95 boxes	£7.20 per box	£684.00
302	470 litres	£10.30 per litre	£4841.00
307	55 rolls	£8.00 per roll	£440.00

MATERIALS REQUISITION

DATE: 20/4/98   DEPT: CP30   NUMBER: 6342

CODE	DESCRIPTION	QUANTITY REQUIRED
307	Paksecure Tape	10 rolls

AUTHORISED: T. Hume

MATERIALS REQUISITION

DATE: 20/4/98   DEPT: CP10   NUMBER: 6343

CODE	DESCRIPTION	QUANTITY REQUIRED
101	Metal Sheets	250 sheets

AUTHORISED: M. Turner

MATERIALS REQUISITION

DATE: 21/4/98   DEPT: CP20   NUMBER: 6344

CODE	DESCRIPTION	QUANTITY REQUIRED
302	Spray paint (grey)	40 litres

AUTHORISED: R. Patton

MATERIALS REQUISITION

DATE: 22/4/98   DEPT: CP10   NUMBER: 6345

CODE	DESCRIPTION	QUANTITY REQUIRED
101	Metal Sheets	320 sheets

AUTHORISED: M. Turner

MATERIALS REQUISITION

DATE: 24/4/98   DEPT: CP10   NUMBER: 6346

CODE	DESCRIPTION	QUANTITY REQUIRED
108	Rivets	10 boxes

AUTHORISED: M. Turner

SALES INVOICE

Metafine Limited

Unit 8 Hall Road Industrial Estate, Newton, NN3 4BH
Tel 01906 765365 Fax 01906 7659112 Email john@metafine.goblin.com
VAT Reg GB 228 6654 78

invoice to

Boxit Limited Victoria Road Deans Hill NN22 2QH	

invoice no	3351
account	4018
your reference	286
date/tax point	21 04 98

deliver to

as above

details	quantity	price	amount (excl VAT)	VAT rate %	VAT amount £
Metal Sheets. Spec 101.	600	19.73	11,838.00	17.5	2,071.65

Total (excl VAT)	11,838.00
VAT	2,071.65
TOTAL	13,909.65

terms
Net 30 days

STORES LEDGER ACCOUNT

Material: Metal sheet

Code: 101

Unit: 1 sheet

Maximum control level: 1,000

Minimum control level: 150

Re-order level: 750

Re-order quantity: 600

DATE	RECEIPTS			ISSUES			STOCK BALANCE		
	Quantity	Unit Price £	Total £	Quantity	Unit Price £	Total £	Quantity	Unit Price £	Total £
17.04.98							350	18.32	6,412

COST LEDGER DATA ENTRY SHEET

Week ending   24 April 1998

Cost centre code	Expenditure code	Amount to be debited £
CP10	M100	
CP20	M100	
CP30	M100	
CP10	M200	
CP20	M200	
CP30	M200	
CS40	M200	
CS50	M200	

Total (check to documents)

MEMORANDUM

To: John Raymond

From: Helen Jones

Date: 28 April 1998

Subject: Standard costing

Part of our reorganisation plans is to put a standard costing system in place. I need an example and some notes to show other staff how this will work. Please prepare these for me as follows:

PRODUCT: METAL SHELF UNIT. Assume that the standard includes 2 sheets of metal (code 101) at £20 per sheet and the budget is for production of 300 units per week.

In the week ended 24 April, 280 units were made, using 570 metal sheets, at a total cost of £10,830.

- as an example, show the calculation of the direct material price and usage variances for the above material for that week

- summarise for me the advantages of standard costing

- give me some suggestions as to the reasons for the variances you have calculated

MEMORANDUM

To:

From:

Date:

Subject:

INTERNAL POLICY DOCUMENT

Issued: 30 November 1997

Subject: **PRODUCTION WAGES**

Construction Department

Direct workers in this department are paid a basic wage of £150 per week, plus a piecework rate of £5 per unit completed.

For example: a worker who makes 10 units earns £150 + £50.

The whole of this amount is treated as direct wages, unless the worker is absent from work, in which case £30 per day's absence is treated as overheads.

Painting Department

Direct workers in this department are paid a basic wage of £250 per 38 hour week. They are also paid a bonus of £6 per hour saved. The standard time allowed is 20 minutes per shelf unit.

The whole of the basic wage is treated as direct wages, unless the worker is absent from work, in which case £50 per day's absence is treated as overheads. The bonus is treated as indirect.

Packing Department

Direct workers are paid on an hourly basis at £4 per hour, up to 40 hours a week. Additional hours worked are paid at time and a half.

TIMESHEET

DEPARTMENT: Construction

EMPLOYEE: E. Fowler   WEEK ENDING: 24/4/98

	MON	TUE	WED	THUR	FRI	TOTAL
HOURS:						
Construction	7.5	8	8	8	7.5	
Absent sick						
Holiday						
Training						
Total Hrs.						
Units Produced	4	6	5	6	5	

TIMESHEET

DEPARTMENT: Painting

EMPLOYEE: R. Patton   WEEK ENDING: 24/4/98

	MON	TUE	WED	THUR	FRI	TOTAL
HOURS:						
Painting	8	8	8	8	6	
Absent sick						
Holiday						
Training						
Total Hrs.						
Units Painted	25	25	26	28	16	

TIMESHEET

DEPARTMENT: Packing

EMPLOYEE: L. Rigg   WEEK ENDING: 24/4/98

	MON	TUE	WED	THUR	FRI	TOTAL
HOURS:						
Packing	6	8.5	8	8	8	
Absent sick						
Holiday						
Training	2.5					
Total Hrs.						
Units Packed	21	32	31	32	30	

CALCULATION AND ANALYSIS OF GROSS WAGES

Calculation

NAME	COST CENTRE CODE	AMOUNT	
E. Fowler	CP10	BASIC	
"	"	PIECEWORK	_____
		TOTAL	
R. Patton	CP20	BASIC	
"	"	BONUS	_____
		TOTAL	
L. Rigg	CP30	BASIC	
"	"	OVERTIME	_____
		TOTAL	

Analysis

NAME	COST CENTRE CODE	EXPENDITURE CODE	AMOUNT
E. Fowler	CP10	W300	
"	"	W400	
R. Patton	CP20	W300	
"	"	W400	
L. Rigg	CP30	W300	
"	"	W400	
		TOTAL	

MEMORANDUM

To:

From:

Date:

Subject:

MEMORANDUM

To: John Raymond

From: Helen Jones

Date: 29 April 1998

Subject: Overheads

Part of our review concerns overheads - apportionment and absorption. As you know, we absorb overheads on labour hours in all three production departments at present, but in the painting department the spray machines are automatic, once set up, so I consider the work to be machine intensive. Also some overheads have been shared equally between the cost centres up to now and I think this could be improved. I started working on all this, but I would like you to finish it and I attach my notes so far.

I did set up the schedules we need - please complete them.

NOTES - OVERHEADS

1 Half year 1/11/97 to 30/4/98 nearly completed.

   Budgeted overheads for 6 months = £131,000

Department	budgeted overheads after allocation & apportionment	Direct Labour Hours
Construction	£52,000	12,500 hrs
Painting	£44,000	2,500 hrs
Packing	£35,000	1,875 hrs

Assume ACTUAL FIGS. for 6 months to 30/4/98 will be as estimated at 27/4/98:

	Actual direct labour hrs
Construction	12,360 hrs
Painting	2,460 hrs
Packing	1,910 hrs

Actual overhead expenditure
for 6 months to 30/4/98 = £132,800.

2 Half year 1/5/98 to 31/10/98 about to start.

Budgeted overheads for 6 months = £131,000, consisting of:

Allocated overhead	Cost Centre
£4,400	CP10
£13,000	CP20
£2,200	CP30
£22,000	CS40
£32,400	CS50

and overheads to be apportioned - improve method?

Heat, light, maintenance of buildings	£18,000
Depreciation and maintenance of machines	£24,000
Other overheads (mainly related to number of staff in dept.)	£15,000

Information available

	CP10	CP20	CP30	CS40	CS50
Floor area (m″)	220	90	50	140	100
NBV of machines (£000s)	140	180	40	30	10
Number of employees	13	3	2	4	8
Administration work (approx.% of total)	50	30	15	5	-
Material requisitions (approx.% of total)	55	25	20	-	-

3 ABSORPTION - CHANGE BASIS FOR PAINTING DEPT. TO MACHINE HOURS. PLANNED MACHINE HOURS = 4,000 HRS. FOR 6 MONTHS.

Construction and Packing - labour hours as in (1).

OVERHEADS SUMMARY FOR FIRST HALF YEAR

Period covered: 1/11/97 to 30/4/98

	CP10	CP20	CP30
Budgeted overheads			
Planned labour hours			
Absorption rate			
Actual labour hours			
Amount absorbed			

Total amount absorbed _____

Total actual overheads _____

*Over/under absorption _____

The corresponding entry in the Overhead Adjustment Account will be *Debit/Credit.
*Delete where not applicable.

OVERHEADS BUDGET FOR SECOND HALF YEAR

Period covered: 1/5/98 to 31/10/98

	CP10	CP20	CP30	CS40	CS50	TOTAL
Allocated overheads						
Heat, light, maintenance of buildings						
Depreciation and maintenance of machines						
Other overheads						
Reapportion: Administration						
Stores						
TOTAL						
Absorption basis						
Absorption rate						

MEMORANDUM

To:

From:

Date:

Subject:

STANDARD COST OF METAL SHELF UNIT

Revised: 30 April 1998

	£	£
DIRECT MATERIALS		
Metal sheets (101) 2 @ £20.00		
Frame (102) 1 set @ £6.00		
Total Direct Material		
DIRECT WAGES		
CP10: 100 minutes @ £7.20 per hour		
CP20: 20 minutes @ £6.90 per hour		
CP30: 15 minutes @ £5.00 per hour		
Total Direct Wages		
PRIME COST		
Overhead absorbed:		
CP10		
CP20 (note: CP20 machine time per unit = 32 minutes)		
CP30		
TOTAL OVERHEADS		
TOTAL STANDARD COST		

MEMORANDUM

To: John Raymond

From: Helen Jones

Date: 30 April 1998

Subject: Sample Variance Report

You have already calculated the material variances for metal sheets for w/e 24/4/98 as an example. I would now like to take this further, as if we had the Standard Costing system fully operational. With the new standard cost and what you had before, complete the Sample Variance Report for me - I have started it. This will be useful in future for comparison.

VARIANCE REPORT					
WEEK ENDING: 24/4/98			PRODUCT: METAL SHELF UNIT		
Cost type	Standard Unit cost	Output	Standard Total cost of output	Actual Total cost	Variance
Direct Material (sheet)		280		10,830	
Direct Material (frame)		280		1,650	
Direct Labour		280		4,508	
Overheads		280		5,200	
Total				22,188	

Costing
Simulation 3
Treetops Limited

suggested time limit 4 hours

SCENARIO

This simulation is based on Treetops Limited, a company which manufactures timber frames for buildings. The tasks include:

- calculation of overhead absorption rates
- calculation of standard cost
- completion of a cost ledger data entry sheet
- calculation and explanation of variances
- dealing with a query about administration overheads

NVQ UNIT 5 – ELEMENTS COVERED

1   record and analyse information relating to direct costs

2   record and analyse information relating to the allocation, apportionment and absorption of overhead costs

3   prepare and present standard cost reports

SIMULATION TREETOPS LIMITED

3

THE SITUATION

INTRODUCTION

Your name is Carol Sims.

You are working in the Administration Section of Treetops Ltd, a company which manufactures timber frames for buildings. Treetops Ltd regularly produces basic frame sections in standard sizes. In addition, Treetops Ltd makes frames to order, the customer having specified the sizes required.

The customers of Treetops Ltd are building contractors, who collect the frames they require. Treetops Ltd does not own delivery vehicles.

The main material used by Treetops Ltd is 100mm x 150mm pre-treated timber, which is purchased in 7m lengths. A stock of this material is kept in the yard, with the stock of finished frame sections.

Other materials used in the assembly of the frames include glue, brackets, nuts, bolts, screws etc. These are all kept in the Stores area of the factory and are referred to in general as "fixings" in the text which follows. The Stores area also contains stocks of packing materials and materials for the maintenance of the machinery.

There is no separate maintenance section. Production workers maintain their own machines.

COST CENTRES

The cost centres are:

Code	Cost Centre
110	Cutting
120	Assembly
130	Goods Outward
140	Stores
150	Administration

Timber is issued from Stores to Cutting, where the sets of correct lengths to make the frames are cut.

Fixings are issued from Stores to Assembly, where the frames are put together in flat sections.

Customers collect frame sections from the Goods Outward section, where the additional fixings which will be required by the builder on site are identified. These are issued to Goods Outward from Stores, together with packing materials, and the Goods Outward worker ensures that the customer's order is packed and is complete.

The Administration Section deals with all aspects of administration of the business, including the accounting function. The Administration Section manages its own stocks of stationery and other office materials.

The Cutting, Assembly, Goods Outward and Stores cost centres come under the supervision of Kevin Grant, the Factory Manager, who joined Treetops Ltd fairly recently.

Toni White is an employee in the Administration Section.

THE COST ACCOUNTING SYSTEM

Treetops Ltd uses standard costing.

When a customer orders non-basic sized frames, job costing is used and the job price is calculated to give a profit margin of 30% of the selling price.

Cost Accounting Codes

Code	Type of cost	Includes
210	Direct Material	Timber only
220	Direct Wages	Work on production of frames in Cutting and Assembly only.
230	Variable Production Overhead	Indirect materials: fixings, packing and maintenance materials.
240	Fixed Production Overhead	Non-production work in Cutting and Assembly. All wages in Goods Outward and Stores. Factory Manager's salary, machine depreciation.
250	Administration Overhead	All administration costs.

After allocation and apportionment, totals for Production Overhead are obtained for Cutting and Assembly. This is done separately for Variable Production Overhead and Fixed Production Overhead.

Direct Labour hours in Cutting and Assembly are used for absorption of production overheads.

All other costs are collected in the administration cost centre and finally absorbed into the cost of sales as a percentage of the total production cost.

THE TASKS TO BE PERFORMED

Tasks 1 and 2 relate to the budget, and determine the absorption rates and the standard cost of a basic frame section. The same absorption rates will be used when job costing is applied.

The remainder of the tasks relate to the period commencing 1 June 1998, to which the budget and standards apply.

1   The date is 11 May 1998. This task relates to calculation of the overhead absorption rates to be used in the year commencing 1 June 1998. You are given two schedules on pages 133 and 134. The first schedule was prepared by Kevin Grant on 5 May 1998 and the second was prepared by Toni White on 7 May 1998. They contain information about the budgeted production overheads and planned amounts of work for the year commencing 1 June 1998.

Using the information given in these schedules, you are required to calculate the total budgeted production overheads for each cost centre and the overhead absorption rates to be used. Your answers should be shown by completing the table on page 135.

2   Treetops Ltd uses a standard costing system. This task relates to the calculation of the Standard Cost of a Basic Frame Section.

Refer to the Memo from Kevin Grant and the Notes from Toni White, both dated 12 May 1998, on page 136. Using the Memo and Notes, together with overhead absorption rates from the table you have prepared in Task 1, complete the Standard Cost Card for Product P541 on page 137.

3   It is now 15 June 1998, ie in the period for which budgets and standards have been prepared in Tasks 1 and 2. A customer, Fabro Ltd, has ordered a set of frames of specified sizes. Refer to the Memo from Kevin Grant on page 138, and to Tasks 1 and 2 where relevant. You are required to complete the Job Card on page 139 and reply to Kevin Grant using the stationery on page 140.

4   Fabro Ltd agreed the price you calculated in Task 3 for Job J001FAB and the work was done in the week ended 26 June 1998. Refer to the Materials Requisitions, Materials Returned Note and Job Sheet on pages 141 and 142 and complete the Cost Ledger Data Entry Sheet on page 142 for the week ending 26 June 1998. You are reminded that the Standard Cost per 7m length of timber is £3.

5   Refer to the Materials Requisitions, Materials Returned Note and Job Sheet, as used in Task 4, and your answer to Task 3. Calculate the Direct Material Usage Variance, Direct Labour Efficiency Variance (Cutting) and Direct Labour Efficiency Variance (Assembly) for Job J001FAB. Using the stationery on page 143, write a Memo to Kevin Grant detailing these variances and explaining the effect each variance will have on the profit for this job.

6   Refer to the Memo from Toni White dated 2 July 1998 on page 144, giving the actual results for Product P541 for the month of June 1998. Refer also to the Standard Cost Card for this product, which you completed in Task 2, on page 137. You are required to calculate all the variances for this product for June 1998, and complete the Variance Report on page 145, including commenting (at the top of page 146) on the possible reasons for the variances and action that could be taken. You are advised to note that standard production cost is being used here, ie before administration overheads were added. You should ignore administration overheads in this Task.

7   Refer to the Memo from Kevin Grant, dated 6 July 1998, on page 146 and write a reply on the stationery on page 147. Your reply should answer all Kevin Grant's questions.

8   On 7 July 1998, you are investigating the Variable overhead expenditure variances for June 1998. Refer to the documents on pages 148 and 149, which you have extracted from the records. The documents relate to Indirect Materials for the week ended 19 June 1998. You are required to check the Cost Ledger Data Entry Sheet and to write a Memo, using the stationery on page 150, querying any unusual items or uncertainties in these documents.

9   This task relates to the administration overheads. You are reminded that all administration costs are collected in the Administration Cost Centre and absorbed into the Cost of Sales at the rate of 11% of Total Production Cost of Goods Sold. Refer to the Memo from Toni White, dated 8 July 1998, on page 151 and write a reply on the stationery on page 152.

TREETOPS LTD

BUDGET FOR THE YEAR 1 JUNE 1998 TO 31 MAY 1999

PRODUCTION OVERHEADS

Prepared by: Kevin Grant   Date: 5 May 1998

Indirect Materials (allocated):

Cost Centre Code	Budget
110	£8,550
120	£116,550
130	£36,000

Indirect Wages (allocated):

Cost Centre Code	Budget
110	£5,155
120	£4,795
130	£8,000
140	£8,000

Planned Direct Labour Hours:

Cost Centre Code	Budget
110	7,500 hours
120	11,250 hours

TREETOPS LTD

BUDGET FOR THE YEAR 1 JUNE 1998 TO 31 MAY 1999

PRODUCTION OVERHEADS

Prepared by: Toni White   Date: 7 May 1998

PRODUCTION OVERHEADS TO BE APPORTIONED

Type of cost	Amount	Basis of apportionment
Factory Manager's salary	£14,400	Number of employees
Depreciation of machines	£33,000	NBV of machinery
Stores (re-apportioned)		Number of Materials requisitions
Goods Outward (re-apportioned)		Equal parts to Cutting and Assembly

COST CENTRES (CODES)

	110	120	130	140
Numbers of employees	4	6	1	1
NBV of machines	£50,000	£20,000	£28,000	£12,000
Number of requisitions	900	360	540	–

Note

Everything is done for variable and fixed overheads separately, so that separate overhead absorption rates are calculated for Variable Overheads and Fixed Overheads, in each of the cost centres 110 (Cutting) and 120 (Assembly).

All overhead absorption rates are based on direct labour hours.

TREETOPS LTD

BUDGET FOR THE YEAR 1 JUNE 1998 TO 31 MAY 1999

PRODUCTION OVERHEADS

Prepared by: Date:

cost centre code	110	120	130	140	
	Cutting	Assembly	Goods Outward	Stores	Total
	£	£	£	£	£
VARIABLE Indirect material					
Goods Outward re-apportioned					
Total	————	————			
	————	————			
Direct Labour hours					
VARIABLE OAR	————	————			
FIXED Indirect Wages					
Factory Manager					
Depreciation					
Stores re-apportioned					
Goods Outward re-apportioned					
TOTAL	————	————			
	————	————			
Direct Labour Hours as above					
FIXED OAR	————	————			
	————	————			

MEMORANDUM

To: Carol Sims

From: Kevin Grant

Date: 12 May 1998

Subject: Standards for Product P541
               (Basic Frame Section Size 5m x 4m)

You will need the following product information to prepare the Standard Cost Card:

Standard for Timber: 5 lengths per frame section

(Code 210: 100mm x 150mm Timber purchased in 7m lengths)

Standard for Direct Labour:

20 minutes in Cutting Department per frame section

30 minutes in Assembly Department per frame section

NOTES

Prepared by: Toni White   **Date:** 12 May 1998

Subject: Standard Cost of Product P541
             (Basic Frame Section Size 5m x 4m)

Standard cost per 7m length of Timber Code 210 is £3.

Standard rates for Direct Labour:

   £5.70 per hour in Cutting Department

   £5.40 per hour in Assembly Department

   (Quantity and times from Kevin)

Administration overheads to be added at a rate of 11% of total Production Cost.

STANDARD COST CARD

Product Name:

Product Code:

Date prepared:

Prepared by:

	£	£
Direct Material: Timber		
_____ lengths @ _____	_____	_____
Direct Labour:		
Cutting _____ hours @ _____	_____	
Assembly _____ hours @ _____	_____	_____
PRIME COST		
Variable Production Overhead:		
Cutting _____ hours @ _____	_____	
Assembly _____ hours @ _____	_____	
Fixed Production Overhead:		
Cutting _____ hours @ _____	_____	
Assembly _____ hours @ _____	_____	_____
TOTAL PRODUCTION COST		
Administration Overheads @ 11%		
		_____
TOTAL COST		
		_____

MEMORANDUM

To: Carol Sims

From: Kevin Grant

Date: 15 June 1998

Subject: Job no. J001FAB

I have calculated the requirements for this Job as follows. Please complete the Job Card and let me know what the price will be, so that I can confirm the order with Fabro Ltd.

The job consists of 8 special sections:

SPECIAL SECTIONS		TIMBER (Code 210)	
Number Required	Size	Each section	Total for job
1	2m x 4m	2 lengths	2 lengths
3	3m x 4m	3 lengths	9 lengths
4	4m x 4m	4 lengths	16 lengths

Direct Labour: each special section takes 30 minutes in Cutting and 36 minutes in Assembly.

TREETOPS LTD
JOB CARD

Job Number: _____   Customer Name: _____

	£	£

Direct Material: Timber

_____ lengths @ _____   _____   _____

Direct Labour:

Cutting _____ hours @ _____   _____

Assembly _____ hours @ _____   _____   _____

PRIME COST

Variable Production Overhead:

Cutting _____ hours @ _____   _____

Assembly _____ hours @ _____   _____

Fixed Production Overhead:

Cutting _____ hours @ _____   _____

Assembly _____ hours @ _____   _____   _____

TOTAL PRODUCTION COST

Administration Overheads @ 11%   _____

TOTAL COST

PROFIT (30% on selling price)   _____

SELLING PRICE   _____

MEMORANDUM

To:

From:

Date:

Subject:

MATERIALS REQUISITION

DATE: 22/6/98   DEPT: 110   NUMBER: 075

CODE	DESCRIPTION	QUANTITY REQUIRED	JOB/PRODUCT
210	100mm x 150mm Timber (7m)	12	J001FAB

AUTHORISED: K.Grant

MATERIALS REQUISITION

DATE: 23/6/98   DEPT: 110   NUMBER: 077

CODE	DESCRIPTION	QUANTITY REQUIRED	JOB/PRODUCT
210	100mm x 150mm Timber (7m)	16	J001FAB

AUTHORISED: K.Grant

MATERIALS RETURNED NOTE

DATE: 26/6/98   DEPT: 110   NUMBER: 038

CODE	DESCRIPTION	QUANTITY RETURNED	JOB/PRODUCT
210	100mm x 150mm Timber (7m)	2	J001FAB

AUTHORISED: K.Grant

TREETOPS LTD

JOB SHEET

Job Number: J001FAB　　　　**Customer:** Fabro Ltd.

Date	Cost Centre	Rate £	Name	Time Worked
22/6/98	110	5.70	P.Remy	45 minutes
22/6/98	110	5.70	S.Benn	1 hour
24/6/98	110	5.70	P.Remy	1 hour
24/6/98	110	5.70	S.Benn	1 hour
25/6/98	120	5.40	S.Lynn	1 hr 40 mins
25/6/98	120	5.40	T.Martinez	1 hr 40 mins
25/6/98	120	5.40	J.Abbey	1 hr 40 mins

COST LEDGER DATA ENTRY SHEET

Week ending:

CODE		AMOUNT	
COST CENTRE	EXPENDITURE	TO BE DEBITED	TO BE CREDITED
		£	£
110	210		
110	220		
120	220		

space for workings

MEMORANDUM

To:

From:

Date:

Subject:

MEMORANDUM

To: Carol Sims

From: Toni White

Date: 2 July 1998

Subject: P541 results for June 1998

To complete the variance report for the above, you will need the following data which I have collected.

The normal production per month is 1,875 units of P541, and therefore planned direct labour hours are 625 hours in Cutting and 937.5 hours in Assembly.

Actual production of P541 was 1,800 units in June 1998.

Timber: 8,980 lengths used, actual cost £27,100.

	Cutting	Assembly
Direct Labour hours	590 hours	925 hours
Direct Labour cost	£3,300	£5,100
Variable overhead cost	£2,450	£10,550
Fixed overhead cost	£3,500	£2,400

space for workings

VARIANCE REPORT

Month:

Product:

Standard Cost per unit:

Report prepared by: **Date:**

	£	£	£
TOTAL STANDARD PRODUCTION COST OF ACTUAL PRODUCTION			
VARIANCES	**F**	**A**	
Direct Material Price			
Direct Material Usage			
Cutting:			
Direct Labour Rate			
Direct Labour Efficiency			
Assembly:			
Direct Labour Rate			
Direct Labour Efficiency			
Cutting:			
Variable Overhead Expenditure			
Variable Overhead Efficiency			
Assembly:			
Variable Overhead Expenditure			
Variable Overhead Efficiency			
Cutting:			
Fixed Overhead Expenditure			
Fixed Overhead Capacity			
Fixed Overhead Efficiency			
Assembly:			
Fixed Overhead Expenditure			
Fixed Overhead Capacity			
Fixed Overhead Efficiency			
TOTAL ACTUAL PRODUCTION COST			

comments on variances

MEMORANDUM

To: Carol Sims

From: Kevin Grant

Date: 6 July 1998

Subject: Variance report, P541 June 1998

I have received your comprehensive variance report and comments and would like you to explain a few points to me:

1. What are the definitions of "Variable" overheads and "Fixed" overheads?

2. I have checked the standard rates for direct labour hours in Cutting and Assembly, but they are not the same per hour as the workers get paid. Toni said they were "inflated" for some reason due to holidays. Can you explain please?

3. There are a lot of variances in the report which are repeated for Cutting and Assembly. Can you tell me what is the benefit of this over having them all put together as if it was one department?

MEMORANDUM

To:

From:

Date:

Subject:

MATERIALS REQUISITION

DATE: 15/6/98   DEPT: 120   NUMBER: 068

CODE	DESCRIPTION	QUANTITY REQUIRED
307	Corner brackets @ £28 per box	50 boxes
AUTHORISED: K.Grant		

MATERIALS REQUISITION

DATE: 16/6/98   DEPT: 110   NUMBER: 069

CODE	DESCRIPTION	QUANTITY REQUIRED
309	Saw blades @ £97 each	4 blades
AUTHORISED: K.Grant		

MATERIALS REQUISITION

DATE: 18/6/98   DEPT: 110   NUMBER: 072

CODE	DESCRIPTION	QUANTITY REQUIRED
302	Heavy Plastic Packing Sheet @ £52 per roll	6 rolls
AUTHORISED: K.Grant		

MATERIALS REQUISITION

DATE: 19/6/98   DEPT: 120   NUMBER: 073

CODE	DESCRIPTION	QUANTITY REQUIRED
305	Nuts & Bolts @ £14 per box	20 boxes

AUTHORISED: K.Grant

MATERIALS REQUISITION

DATE: 19/6/98   DEPT: 130   NUMBER: 074

CODE	DESCRIPTION	QUANTITY REQUIRED
308	Packing Tape @ £22 per roll	10 rolls

AUTHORISED: K.Grant

COST LEDGER DATA ENTRY SHEET

Week ending: 19 June 1998

CODE		AMOUNT	
COST CENTRE	EXPENDITURE	TO BE DEBITED	TO BE CREDITED
		£	£
110	230	980	
120	230	1,400	
130	230	220	

MEMORANDUM

To:

From:

Date:

Subject:

MEMORANDUM

To: Carol Sims

From: Toni White

Date: 8 July 1998

Subject: Administration Overheads

I have been looking at the Administration Overhead Account for the month of June 1998. The total actual expenditure which has been coded to this account during June is £6,610 and the amount absorbed using the 11% rate is £5,966. I do not quite understand what this difference is and what caused it. Could you explain it to me, please? Also what double entry is needed to deal with it?

MEMORANDUM

To:

From:

Date:

Subject

Reports & Returns Simulation 1

Hoddle Limited

reproduced by kind permission of AAT

suggested time limit 3 hours

SCENARIO

This simulation is based on Hoddle Limited, a company which prints cards, brochures and booklets. Sometimes it contracts out work to Kelly Limited, another company in the same group. The tasks include:

- preparation of a VAT Return from the accounting records
- dealing with queries involving VAT
- consolidating the profit and loss accounts for Hoddle Ltd and Kelly Ltd
- preparing an internal report presenting key ratios and performance indicators
- preparation of an interfirm comparison form

NVQ UNIT 6 – ELEMENTS COVERED

1 prepare and present periodic performance reports
2 prepare reports and returns for outside agencies
3 prepare VAT returns

SIMULATION HODDLE LIMITED

THE SITUATION

Your name is Sol Bellcamp and you work as an accounts assistant for a printing company, Hoddle Limited. Hoddle Limited is owned 100 per cent by another printing company, Kelly Limited. You report to the Group Accountant, Sherry Teddingham.

Hoddle Limited manufactures a wide range of printed materials such as cards, brochures and booklets. Most customers are based in the UK, but sales are also made to other countries in the European Union (EU). There are no exports to countries outside the EU. All the company's purchases come from businesses within the UK.

Hoddle Limited is registered for VAT and it makes both standard-rated and zero-rated supplies to its UK customers. All sales to other EU countries qualify as zero-rated. The company's local VAT office is at Bredon House, 14 Abbey Street, Pexley PY2 3WR.

Kelly Limited is separately registered for VAT; there is no group registration in force. Both companies have an accounting year ending on 31 March. There are no other companies in the Kelly group.

Hoddle Limited is a relatively small company and sometimes suffers from shortage of capacity to complete customers' jobs. In these cases, the printing work is done by Kelly Limited. Kelly then sells the completed products to Hoddle for onward sale to the customer. The sale from Kelly to Hoddle is recorded in the books of each company at cost; Kelly does not charge a profit margin.

In this simulation you are concerned with the accounting year ended 31 March 1998.

- To begin with you will be required to prepare the VAT return for Hoddle Limited in respect of the quarter ended 31 March 1998.

- You will then be required to prepare certain reports, both for internal use and for an external interfirm comparison scheme, covering the whole accounting year ended 31 March 1998. These reports will treat the two companies as a single group; they will contain consolidated figures, not figures for either of the two companies separately.

Today's date is 9 April 1998.

THE TASKS TO BE COMPLETED

1 Refer to the documents on pages 156 and 157; these have been received from Hoddle Ltd's suppliers during March 1998. No entries have yet been made in Hoddle Ltd's books of account in respect of these documents. You are required to explain how you will deal with them when preparing Hoddle Ltd's VAT return for the period January to March 1998. Use the blank page 158.

2 Refer to the sales day book summary, purchases day book summary, cash book summary and petty cash book summary on pages 159 and 160. These have been printed out from Hoddle Ltd's computerised accounting system for the period January to March 1998. (You are reminded that these summaries do not include the documents dealt with in Task 1.) Refer also to the memo on page 161. Using this information you are required to complete the VAT return of Hoddle Limited for the quarter ended 31 March 1998. A blank VAT return is provided on page 162.

3 The Group Accountant is considering adoption of the cash accounting scheme for VAT. He believes that Hoddle Limited (though not Kelly Limited) might qualify for the scheme. He has asked you to draft a letter to the VAT office, in his name, requesting certain details of the scheme. He is interested in the turnover limit for the scheme, particularly since Hoddle is a member of a group of companies, and he wants to know how the scheme affects a company in its dealings with bad debts. You are required to draft this letter using the blank letterhead on page 163.

4 Refer to the profit and loss account of Kelly Limited on page 164, which covers the period 1 January to 31 March 1998. You are required to prepare a profit and loss account for the same period in which the results of Hoddle and Kelly are consolidated. Enter your answer on the form provided on page 165, as follows:

- Enter the results of Kelly Ltd in the first column of the form.

- Using the information already provided for earlier tasks construct the results of Hoddle Ltd and enter them in the second column. Note that Hoddle Ltd's stock at 1 January 1998 was valued at £14,638, while stock at 31 March 1998 was valued at £16,052.

- Make the appropriate adjustments in the third column to eliminate the effects of trading between Kelly Ltd and Hoddle Ltd.

- Calculate the consolidated figures and enter them in the fourth column.

5 Refer to the information on pages 166 to 168. Using this, and information already provided for earlier tasks, you are required to prepare a report for the Accountant on the group results for the year ended 31 March 1998. Your report should contain the following:

- Key ratios: gross profit margin; net profit margin; return on shareholders' capital employed.

- Sales revenue for each quarter; both in actual terms and indexed to a common base.

- A pie chart showing the proportion of annual (unindexed) sales earned in each quarter.

Use your own stationery to set out your answer. Note that you are not required to comment on the results for the year, merely to present them according to the instructions above.

6 You are required to complete the interfirm comparison form on page 169.

7 You are required to prepare a memo to the Group Accountant enclosing the interfirm comparison form for authorisation before despatch. Use the form on page 170.

Engineering Supplies Limited

Haddlefield Road, Blaysley CG6 6AW
Tel/fax: 01376 44531

Hoddle Limited
22 Formguard Street
Pexley
PY6 3QW

SALES INVOICE NO: *2155*

Date: *27 March 1998*

£

VAT omitted in error from invoice no 2139

£2,667.30 @ 17.5%

466.77

Total due

466.77

Terms: net 30 days

VAT registration: 318 1827 58

Alpha Stationery

Ainsdale Centre, Mexton EV1 4DF
Telephone 01392 43215

26-Mar-98

1 box transparent folders: red

Total incl VAT @17.5%	14.84
Amount tendered	20.00
Change	5.16

VAT registration: 356 7612 33

JAMIESON & CO

Jamieson House, Baines Road, Gresham GM7 2PQ
Telephone: 01677 35567   Fax: 01677 57640

PROFORMA SALES INVOICE

VAT registration: *412 7553 67*

Hoddle Limited
22 Formguard Street
Pexley
PY6 3QW

	£
For professional services in connection with debt collection	
Our fees	350.00
VAT	61.25
Total due	411.25

A VAT invoice will be submitted when the total due is paid in full.

answers to Task 1

HODDLE LIMITED: SALES DAY BOOK SUMMARY
JANUARY TO MARCH 1998

	JAN	FEB	MAR	TOTAL
	£	£	£	£
UK: ZERO RATED	20,091.12	22,397.00	23,018.55	65,506.67
UK: STANDARD-RATED	15,682.30	12,914.03	15,632.98	44,229.31
OTHER EU	874.12	4,992.66	5,003.82	10,870.60
VAT	2,744.40	2,259.95	2,735.77	7,740.12
TOTAL	39,391.94	42,563.64	46,391.12	128,346.70

HODDLE LIMITED: PURCHASES DAY BOOK SUMMARY
JANUARY TO MARCH 1998

	JAN	FEB	MAR	TOTAL
	£	£	£	£
PURCHASES	14,532.11	20,914.33	15,461.77	50,908.21*
DISTRIBUTION EXPENSES	4,229.04	3,761.20	5,221.43	13,211.67
ADMIN EXPENSES	5,123.08	2,871.45	3,681.62	11,676.15
OTHER EXPENSES	1,231.00	1,154.99	997.65	3,383.64
VAT	4,027.97	4,543.22	4,119.34	12,690.53
TOTAL	29,143.20	33,245.19	29,481.81	91,870.20

*This figure includes £18,271 of purchases from Kelly Limited.

HODDLE LIMITED: CASH BOOK SUMMARY
JANUARY TO MARCH 1998

	JAN	FEB	MAR	TOTAL
	£	£	£	£
PAYMENTS				
TO CREDITORS	12,901.37	15,312.70	18,712.44	46,926.51
TO PETTY CASH	601.40	555.08	623.81	1,780.29
WAGES/SALARIES	5,882.18	6,017.98	66,114.31	18,014.47
TOTAL	19,384.95	21,885.76	25,450.56	66,721.27
RECEIPTS				
VAT FROM CUSTOMS &				
EXCISE	2,998.01			2,998.01
FROM CUSTOMERS	29,312.44	34,216.08	36,108.77	99,637.29
TOTAL	32,310.45	34,216.08	36,108.77	102,635.30
SURPLUS FOR MONTH	12,925.50	12,330.32	10,658.21	
BALANCE B/F	-8,712.41	4,213.09	16,543.41	
BALANCE C/F	4,213.09	16,543.41	27,201.62	

HODDLE LIMITED: PETTY CASH BOOK SUMMARY
JANUARY TO MARCH 1998

	JAN	FEB	MAR	TOTAL
	£	£	£	£
PAYMENTS				
STATIONERY	213.85	80.12	237.58	531.55
TRAVEL	87.34	76.50	102.70	266.54
OFFICE EXPENSES	213.66	324.08	199.51	737.25
VAT	86.55	74.38	84.02	244.95
TOTAL	601.40	555.08	623.81	1,780.29
RECEIPTS				
FROM CASH BOOK	601.40	555.08	623.81	1,780.29
SURPLUS FOR MONTH	0.00	0.00	0.00	
BALANCE B/F	200.00	200.00	200.00	
BALANCES C/F	200.00	200.00	200.00	

MEMORANDUM

To:	Sol Bellcamp
From:	Sherry Teddingham
Date:	6 April 1998
Subject:	Bad Debt - Batty Limited

As you probably know, we have had great difficulty in persuading the above customer to pay what he owes us. We invoiced him in July 1997 (on 30 days terms) for £420 plus VAT at the standard rate, but he has always disputed the debt and it looks as though we will never recover it. We wrote it off to the bad debt account in March of this year, so you should take this into account when preparing the VAT return for the quarter just ended.

SPECIMEN

Value Added Tax Return

For the period
01 01 98 to 31 03 98

HM Customs
and Excise

For Official Use

081 578 4060 19 100 03 98   Q35192
MR SHERRY TEDDINGHAM
HODDLE LIMITED
22 FORMGUARD STREET
PEXLEY
PY6 3QW   219921/10

Your VAT Office telephone number is 01682 386000

Registration Number	Period
578 4060 19	03 98

You could be liable to a financial penalty if your completed return and all the VAT payable are not received by the due date.

Due date: 30 04 98

For
Official
Use

Before you fill in this form please read the notes on the back and the VAT leaflet *"Filling in your VAT return"*. Fill in all boxes clearly in ink, and write 'none' where necessary. Don't put a dash or leave any box blank. If there are no pence write "00" in the pence column. Do not enter more than one amount in any box.

For official use		£	p
VAT due in this period on **sales** and other outputs	**1**		
VAT due in this period on **acquisitions** from other **EC Member States**	**2**		
Total VAT due **(the sum of boxes 1 and 2)**	**3**		
VAT reclaimed in this period on **purchases** and other inputs (including acquisitions from the EC)	**4**		
Net VAT to be paid to Customs or reclaimed by you **(Difference between boxes 3 and 4)**	**5**		
Total value of **sales** and all other outputs excluding any VAT. **Include your box 8 figure**	**6**		00
Total value of **purchases** and all other inputs excluding any VAT. **Include your box 9 figure**	**7**		00
Total value of all **supplies** of goods and related services, excluding any VAT, to other **EC Member States**	**8**		00
Total value of all **acquisitions** of goods and related services, excluding any VAT, from other **EC Member States**	**9**		00

Retail schemes. If you have used any of the schemes in the period covered by this return, enter the relevant letter(s) in this box.

If you are enclosing a payment please tick this box.

DECLARATION: You, or someone on your behalf, must sign below.

I, ...declare that the
(Full name of signatory in BLOCK LETTERS)
information given above is true and complete.

Signature ....Date ....19...............

A false declaration can result in prosecution.

B

0196929   PCU(November 1995)

VAT 100 (Half)

HODDLE LIMITED

22 Formguard Street
Pexley
PY6 3QW

Tel 01682 431256 Fax 01682 431874 E-mail Glyn@Hoddle.amtrex.com
VAT Reg 578 4060 19

Registered Office: 22 Formguard Street, Pexley, PY6 3QW. Registered in England No 2314561

KELLY LIMITED
PROFIT AND LOSS ACCOUNT
FOR THE THREE MONTHS ENDED 31 MARCH 1998

	£	£
Sales to external customers		275,601
Sales to Hoddle Limited at cost		20,167*
Total sales		295,768
Opening Stock	28,341	
Purchases	136,095	
	164,436	
Closing Stock	31,207	
Cost of sales		133,229
Gross profit		162,539
Wages and salaries	47,918	
Distribution expenses	28,341	
Administration expenses	30,189	
Stationery	2,541	
Travel	2,001	
Office expenses	3,908	
Interest payable	12,017	
Other expenses	11,765	
		138,680
Net profit for the period		23,859

*This figure includes £1,896 in respect of a job completed on 31 March 1998 but not delivered to Hoddle Limited until 1 April 1998. It is not included in Hoddle Ltd's purchases for the period ended 31 March.

KELLY LTD AND HODDLE LTD CONSOLIDATED PROFIT AND LOSS ACCOUNT

FOR THE THREE MONTHS ENDED 31 MARCH 1998

	Kelly £	Hoddle £	Adjustments £	Consolidated £
Sales				
Opening stock				
Purchases				
Closing stock				
Cost of sales				
Gross profit				
Wages and salaries				
Distribution expenses				
Administration expenses				
Stationery				
Travel				
Office expenses				
Interest payable				
Other expenses				
TOTAL				
Net profit for the period				

KELLY LTD AND HODDLE LTD
CONSOLIDATED BALANCE SHEET AT 31 MARCH 1998

	£	£	£
Fixed assets at net book value			1,229,348
Current assets			
Stock		49,155	
Trade debtors		223,009	
VAT recoverable		13,451	
Cash at bank and in hand		40,088	
		325,703	
Current liabilities			
Trade creditors	136,531		
Other creditors	11,740		
		148,271	
Net current assets			177,432
			1,406,780
Long-term liability			
Loan repayable in 2004			(372,072)
			1,034,708
FINANCED BY			
Capital and reserves			
Called up share capital			234,167
Retained profits			800,541
			1,034,708

KELLY LTD AND HODDLE LTD: QUARTERLY CONSOLIDATED PROFIT AND LOSS ACCOUNTS
FOR THE YEAR ENDED 31 MARCH 1998

	1 Apr 1997- 30 Jun 1997 £	1 Jul 1997- 30 Sep 1997 £	1 Oct 1997- 31 Dec 1997 £	1 Jan 1998- 31 Mar 1998 £	1 Apr 1997- 31 Mar 1998 £
Sales	325,719	275,230	306,321		
Cost of sales	134,861	109,421	121,358		
Gross profit	190,858	165,809	184,963		
Wages and salaries	63,314	61,167	64,412		
Distribution expenses	34,217	30,135	31,221		
Administration expenses	34,765	33,012	36,415		
Stationery	2,981	2,671	3,008		
Travel	1,975	1,876	2,413		
Office expenses	4,412	4,713	3,083		
Interest payable	12,913	12,714	12,432		
Other expenses	10,981	16,421	15,431		
	165,558	162,709	168,415		
Net profit for the period	25,300	3,100	16,548		

Note to students: complete the above schedule by filling in the figures for the final quarter in the fourth column and totalling the figures for the year in the fifth column.

MEMORANDUM

To: Sol Bellcamp

From: Sherry Teddingham

Subject: Adjusting for the effects of price rises

Date: 2 April 1998

When presenting your quarterly reports on group results please include an item of information additional to that which you normally present. As well as noting sales revenue by quarter, please present quarterly sales revenue adjusted to take account of price rises.

I have identified a suitable index as follows:

First quarter 1996/97 (base period)	231.8
First quarter 1997/98	239.3
Second quarter 1997/98	241.5
Third quarter 1997/98	244.0
Fourth quarter 1997/98	241.8

I will keep you informed of future movements in this index.

INTERFIRM COMPARISON DATA

Name of company ....

Year ended ....

DATA	£	% of sales	Industry best	Industry average
Sales				
Gross Profit			62.1%	57.3%
Net Profit			10.4%	5.8%
Fixed Assets				
Current assets				
Current Liabilities				
Return on Capital Employed			10.3%	9.0%

NOTES ON COMPLETION OF FORM

- Enter figures in the blank white boxes.

- 'Sales' means sales to external customers. Inter-company, inter-divisional or inter-branch sales should be excluded.

- Fixed assets should be stated at net book value.

- Return on capital employed is net profit before interest charges, divided by the total of fixed assets (stated at net book value) and net current assets.

MEMORANDUM

To:

From:

Date:

Subject:

Reports & Returns Simulation 2

Libra Publishing

suggested time limit 3 hours

SCENARIO

This simulation is based on Libra Publishing, a company which publishes educational books and computer software. The tasks include:

- preparation of a VAT Return from the accounting records
- dealing with queries involving VAT
- consolidating the profit and loss accounts for the two operating divisions: Libra Books and Libra Software
- preparing an internal report presenting key ratios from financial statements
- preparation of an external financial report to a lending bank

NVQ UNIT 6 – ELEMENTS COVERED

1   prepare and present periodic performance reports
2   prepare reports and returns for outside agencies
3   prepare VAT returns

SIMULATION
LIBRA PUBLISHING

2

THE SITUATION

Your name is Thomas Handy. You work as an Accounting Technician for a publishing company, Libra Publishing. You report to the Finance Director, William Collins.

Libra Publishing produces educational books which it distributes to colleges and schools throughout the UK. It has also diversified into producing CD ROMs and software which it sells into the educational market. Most of its customers are UK-based educational establishments, but sales are also made to English schools and colleges in the EU.

At the beginning of the financial year (1 July 1998) Libra Publishing was divided into two operating divisions: Libra Books and Libra Software. During the year Libra Publishing expanded its mail order sales, partly through its website. This resulted in a large increase in cash sales, particularly of educational software.

All the company's purchases are supplied from businesses within the UK. Libra Publishing operates from a unit on an industrial estate. The address is Unit 12 Oldwood Industrial Estate, Melbury Road, Casterbridge CB2 3GH.

Libra Publishing Limited is registered for VAT and it makes both standard-rated supplies (software) and zero-rated supplies (books) to its UK customers. All sales to other EU countries qualify as zero-rated. The company's local VAT office is at Mellstock House, The Parade, Casterbridge CB1 4TH.

In this simulation you are concerned with the accounting year ended 30 June 1999.

There are two series of tasks in this simulation:

1   The preparation of data for the VAT Return for Libra Publishing Limited (incorporating both publishing divisions) for the VAT quarter ending 30 June 1999.

2   The preparation of data for reports due at the end of the financial year: an internal financial report consolidating the figures for the two operating divisions and an external report of financial data for Centro Bank Plc from which Libra Publishing is borrowing £60,000.

The date is 5 July 1999.

During the course of the week a new trainee, Kerry Gold, will be working with you to learn the procedures and gain experience of the queries and problems that inevitably arise from time-to-time.

THE TASKS TO BE COMPLETED

1   Bella Donn, the Marketing Director of Libra Software has just produced an educational package which includes a textbook and a CD ROM disk which are film-wrapped together. The planned launch date is 1 August. Normally books are zero-rated for VAT and CDs are standard-rated. She asks you as the office VAT expert: "Is VAT chargeable on the whole pack, or just part of it?" You telephone the local VAT office to find out and they ask you to send in a sample of the package so that they can assess the VAT liability. You are to draft a letter (which will accompany the sample package) to the VAT Office on the letterhead shown on page 174. The address to write to is HM Customs & Excise, Mellstock House, The Parade, Casterbridge CB1 4TH. The person you spoke to on the telephone at the VAT Office on 2 July was Miss Annie Day. The letter should be prepared for the signature of Damon Wildene, Accounts Manager.

2   A computer printout of bad debts written off and put through Bad Debts Written Off Account is handed to you (see page 175). The list is headed "Information – for the VAT return". List and total on page 175 the bad debts you will claim relief for in the VAT return for the quarter ending 30 June 1999. Note that all goods are despatched within two working days of the invoice date.

3   On page 176 there are a number of summaries for the last VAT quarter, which need completing:
   •   the sales day book summary (already adjusted for bad debts written off)
   •   purchases day book summary
   •   cash book and petty cash book summaries
   On page 177 there is a schedule of further data collected for the VAT return.
   The figures are for both operating divisions of Libra Publishing – they have been consolidated.
   Using this information you are required to draw up a VAT Control Account for Libra Publishing for the VAT quarter ending 30 June 1999. Use the VAT Control Account set out on page 177.

4   With the data you now have compiled, you are to complete the VAT return of Libra Publishing Limited for the quarter ended 30 June 1999. A blank VAT 100 is provided on page 178. The form should be prepared for the signature of William Collins and left undated.

5   Kerry (the trainee) asks "When has the form got to be sent off? What would happen if someone forgot to send it off by the due date?" Write down on page 179 your reply to these two questions.

6   The schedule on page 180 sets out the profit and loss figures for Libra Books and Libra Software for the financial year to 30 June 1999. You are required to calculate the profit and loss results for the two divisions, and then consolidate the results. You must adjust for the internal sale by Libra Books of computer manuals to Libra Software at an internal transfer price of £25,000. The columns on page 180 are for the two sets of divisional figures (columns 1 & 2), the adjustments for the internal transfer (column 3) and the consolidated results (column 4). Assume that all the transferred stock of computer manuals has been sold.

7   A draft balance sheet for Libra Publishing Limited is shown on page 181. Using this, and the consolidated profit and loss account (page 180), you are required to complete a schedule (page 182) comparing the company's key ratios and performance indicators for 1998 and 1999.

8   Using the completed schedule on page 182 you are to draw up a compound bar chart showing the sales, gross profit and net profit for the two years. Graph paper is provided on page 183.

9   Libra Publishing has a £60,000 long-term bank loan from Centro Bank Plc. As part of the terms of the loan it has to send in regular reports of its current assets and current liabilities figures. These provide the bank with an indication of the company's ability to repay the loan. The more funds the company has available in its hands, or due in the short term, the more able it is to repay the loan. Complete the pro-forma return to Centro Bank (page 184) with data from the balance sheet.

LIBRA PUBLISHING

Unit 12 Oldwood Industrial Estate, Melbury Road, Casterbridge CB2 3GH

Tel 01603 289424 Fax 01603 289777 E-mail books@libra.u-mail.com
VAT Reg GB 5463 7652 65

Libra Publishing Limited, Registered in England No 0344748

Information – for the VAT Return – all posted to Bad Debts A/c 30.6.99

BAD DEBTS WRITTEN OFF 30 JUNE 1999

invoice date	invoice due	debtor	net amount (£)	VAT amount (£)
30.08.98	30.09.98	Verey Computers	400.00	70.00
16.09.98	31.10.98	Holbein Bookshop	678.90	nil
19.10.98	31.11.98	Bacon Books	567.95	nil
05.11.98	05.12.98	ComputaVision	66.75	11.68
12.12.98	31.12.98	CD Supplies Ltd	341.00	59.67
15.12.98	15.01.99	Roman Software	672.50	117.68
07.01.99	28.02.99	Bretherton Books	562.50	nil
12.03.99	30.04.99	Iris School Supplies	450.00	78.75
01.04.99	30.04.99	Bitstream Ltd	256.00	44.80

VAT – BAD DEBT RELIEF LISTING

VAT Return for quarter April - June 1999

invoice date	invoice due	debtor	net amount (£)	VAT amount (£)
TOTAL				£

LIBRA LIMITED: SALES DAY BOOK SUMMARY
01 April to 30 June 1999

	April £	May £	June £	TOTAL £
UK Zero-rated	70,654.34	65,723.90	69,674.11	
UK standard-rated	5,678.90	7,845.12	6,982.56	
EU sales (non-UK)	453.78	1,117.60	231.90	
VAT	993.80	1,372.89	1,221.94	

LIBRA LIMITED: PURCHASES DAY BOOK SUMMARY
01 April to 30 June 1999

	April £	May £	June £	TOTAL £
Purchases/Expenses	45,786.25	36,567.80	50,786.12	
VAT	2,675.78	1,856.60	3,456.60	

LIBRA LIMITED: CASH BOOK SUMMARY – NON CREDIT ITEMS
01 April to 30 June 1999

	April £	May £	June £	TOTAL £
PAYMENTS				
Cash Purchases	1,341.75	3,890.00	2,873.45	
VAT	234.80	680.75	502.85	
RECEIPTS				
Cash Sales	12,360.00	7,930.88	11,703.67	
VAT	1,348.90	983.40	1,156.75	

LIBRA LIMITED:PETTY CASH BOOK SUMMARY
01 April to 30 June 1999

	April £	May £	June £	TOTAL £
Purchases/Expenses	239.90	198.75	310.70	
VAT	28.70	23.76	35.20	

Libra Publishing: VAT 100 data

VAT quarter 04-06/99

Sales Credit Notes	Net £2,560.00, VAT £245.00
Suppliers' Credit Notes	Net £1,260.00, VAT £145.50
Previous periods' errors	VAT underpaid 09-12/98 £60.60
EU Acquisitions	None
Other notes	None

VATControl Account: Libra Publishing Limited			
VAT deductible: input tax		**VAT payable: output tax**	
	£		£
Purchases Day Book		Sales Day Book	
less credit notes		*less* credit notes	
Cash Book		Cash Book	
Petty Cash Book			
EU Acquisitions		EU Acquisitions	
Correction of error		Correction of error	
Bad debt relief			
TOTAL INPUT TAX		TOTAL OUTPUT TAX	
		less TOTAL INPUT TAX	
		equals VAT DUE	

SPECIMEN

Value Added Tax Return

For the period

01 04 99 to 30 06 99

HM Customs
and Excise

625 454 7108 51 100 03 99 Q25147

LIBRA PUBLISHING LIMITED
UNIT 12 OLDWOOD INDUSTRIAL ESTATE
MELBURY ROAD
CASTERBRIDGE
CB2 3GH

For Official Use

Registration Number	Period
5463 7652 65	06 99

You could be liable to a financial penalty if your completed return and all the VAT payable are not received by the due date.

Due date: **31 07 99**

For
Official
Use

Before you fill in this form please read the notes on the back and the VAT leaflet *"Filling in your VAT return"*. Fill in all boxes clearly in ink, and write 'none' where necessary. Don't put a dash or leave any box blank. If there are no pence write "00" in the pence column. Do not enter more than one amount in any box.

For official use			£	p
	VAT due in this period on **sales** and other outputs	**1**		
	VAT due in this period on **acquisitions** from other **EC Member States**	**2**		
	Total VAT due **(the sum of boxes 1 and 2)**	**3**		
	VAT reclaimed in this period on **purchases** and other inputs (including acquisitions from the EC)	**4**		
	Net VAT to be paid to Customs or reclaimed by you **(Difference between boxes 3 and 4)**	**5**		
	Total value of **sales** and all other outputs excluding any VAT. **Include your box 8 figure**	**6**		00
	Total value of **purchases** and all other inputs excluding any VAT. **Include your box 9 figure**	**7**		00
	Total value of all **supplies** of goods and related services, excluding any VAT, to other **EC Member States**	**8**		00
	Total value of all **acquisitions** of goods and related services, excluding any VAT, from other **EC Member States**	**9**		00

Retail schemes. If you have used any of the schemes in the period covered by this return, enter the relevant letter(s) in this box.

If you are enclosing a payment please tick this box.

DECLARATION: You, or someone on your behalf, must sign below.

I, ...declare that the
(Full name of signatory in BLOCK LETTERS)
information given above is true and complete.

Signature ....Date ....19................

A false declaration can result in prosecution.

B

0196929   PCU(November 1995)

VAT 100 (Half)

answers to Kerry's questions

LIBRA PUBLISHING LIMITED

PROFIT AND LOSS ACCOUNT FOR THE YEAR ENDED 30 JUNE 1999

	BOOKS DIVISION £	SOFTWARE DIVISION £	ADJUSTMENTS £	CONSOLIDATED FIGURES £
Sales	856,050	155,900		
Opening stock	75,800	56,890		
Purchases	565,300	75,900		
Closing stock	79,585	67,812		
Cost of sales				
Gross profit				
Wages and salaries	101,856	35,670		
Distribution expenses	25,678	5,671		
Administration expenses	3,475	1,205		
Marketing	5,786	4,675		
R&D	2,500	4,700		
Royalties	65,561	10,652		
Interest payable	2,563	456		
Other expenses	267	571		
TOTAL				
Net profit for the period				

LIBRA PUBLISHING LIMITED
Balance Sheet as at 30 June 1999

	£	£	£
Fixed assets at net book value			1,521,700
Current assets			
Stock		147,397	
Trade debtors		176,493	
VAT		2,598	
Bank		45,600	
		372,088	
Current liabilities			
Trade creditors	259,671		
Royalties due	35,600		
Other creditors	12,362		
		307,633	
Net current assets			64,455
Long-term bank loan			(60,000)
			1,526,155
FINANCED BY			
Capital and reserves			
Called up share capital			1,000,000
Profit and loss			526,155
			1,526,155

LIBRA PUBLISHING LIMITED

COMPARATIVE KEY FIGURES AND RATIOS

FINANCIAL YEARS ENDED 30 JUNE 1998 & 1999

	1998	1999	% change (+ or −)
Sales	£859,625		
Gross Profit	£315,870		
Gross Profit Ratio	37%		
Net Profit	£101,120		
Net Profit Ratio	12%		
Capital & Reserves	£1,411,984		
Return on Capital Employed*	7%		

Notes

*Formula: Return on Capital Employed =

$$\frac{\text{net profit}}{\text{capital and reserves}} \times 100$$

Calculate percentages to the
nearest percentage point.

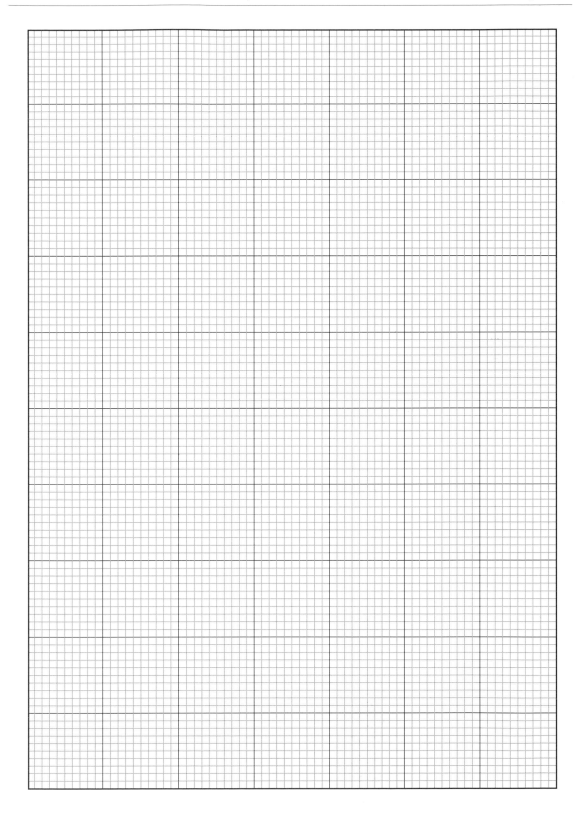

CENTRO BANK PLC

Current Position Return

Business Name ....

Date ....

CURRENT ASSETS

£

Stock Held

Trade Debtors

VAT reclaimable

Bank Balance

Other

TOTAL CURRENT ASSETS   £ _____ 1

CURRENT LIABILITIES

£

Trade Creditors

VAT due

Bank Overdraft

Other amounts payable

TOTAL CURRENT LIABILITIES   £ _____ 2

WORKING CAPITAL SURPLUS
(CURRENT ASSETS LESS CURRENT LIABILITIES)   £ _____ 1–2

Central Assessment Tasks

Tamworth Limited

The tasks in Sections 1 and 2 of this Central Assessment were issued by AAT in December 1996. Following the introduction of the revised Unit 5 'Recording Cost Information' in 1998, Osborne Books has added a new Section 3 covering the expansion of the specifications.

The tasks in Sections 1 and 2 are reproduced by kind permission of AAT.

The tasks in Section 3 have been provided by Roger Petheram.

It is recommended that students spend three hours completing the tasks, allocating the time as follows:

Section 1	75 minutes
Section 2	45 minutes
Section 3	60 minutes

Please note that from December 1999 the Central Assessment for this Unit will be set out in two sections. The content and approach remain the same.

SECTION 1

It is recommended that you spend approximately 1 hour 15 minutes on this section.

DATA

You are employed as an accounting technician by Tamworth Limited and you report to the management accountant. Tamworth Ltd is a medium-sized company employing 760 people at a factory in Northern England; it is primarily engaged in the manufacture of a bathroom accessory.

You have been given a number of tasks concerned with the performance of the cutting, moulding, finishing and packaging departments for the year ended 30 November 1996.

Tamworth Ltd has a budgetary control system and uses standard costing. You have been given the following budget and actual performance data.

Year ended 30 November 1996				
Department	Cutting	Moulding	Finishing	Packaging
Budgeted production (units)	379,000	356,000	362,100	375,000
Standard time per unit	6 mins	7.5 mins	8 mins	4 mins
Budgeted wage rate per hour	£5.25	£4.60	£5.10	£5.05
Actual production (units)	376,400	353,200	364,125	372,825
Actual wages	£200,956	£197,823	£247,720	£124,000
Actual labour hours worked	37,214	41,213	45,874	24,315
Average number of workers	164	173	162	195
Workers leaving during the year	35	14	11	13

Task 1.1

The production manager, who has responsibility for all four departments, is concerned about staff retention rates.

(a)   Complete the table shown below using data from page 186.

Note: round off your workings to one decimal place.

Department:	Cutting	Moulding	Finishing	Packaging
Average number of workers				
Workers leaving during the year				
% staff leaving 1996				
% staff leaving 1995	12.1	7.8	7.3	7.4

(b)   Write a memorandum to the production manager using the form on the next page:

•   analysing your results from Task 1.1(a)

•   highlighting areas of concern and possible causes

•   explaining the potential costs and consequences for the company

MEMORANDUM

To:

From:

Subject: **Date:**

Task 1.2

The management accountant is keen to inform the packaging department of its efficiency and capacity performance in relation to other departments.

(a)   Using the data from page 186, you have been asked by the management accountant to complete the following table for the packaging department.

Note: round off your ratio workings to one decimal place.

Department	Cutting	Moulding	Finishing	Packaging
Budgeted production (hours)	37,900	44,500	48,280	
Actual labour hours worked	37,214	41,213	45,874	
Standard hours produced	37,640	44,150	48,550	
Capacity ratio	98.2%	92.6%	95.0%	
Efficiency ratio	101.1%	107.1%	105.8%	

$$\text{Capacity ratio} \quad = \quad \frac{\text{Actual labour hours worked}}{\text{Budget hours}}$$

$$\text{Efficiency ratio} \quad = \quad \frac{\text{Standard hours produced}}{\text{Actual labour hours worked}}$$

(b)   Write a note to the packaging department supervisor explaining the results of his department and giving possible reasons. The stationery for the note is on the next page.

NOTE

To:

From:

Subject: **Date:**

Task 1.3

The production manager is considering purchasing a new cutting machine for the cutting department. The cost of the machine is likely to be £180,000 and it will have a life of approximately five years and scrap value of between £10,000 and £15,000. Past experience has shown that such machinery will lose value and have most usage in the early part of its life.

Write a report to the production manager using the stationery on pages 192 and 193 detailing:

- the method of depreciation that should be used

- an approximate rate that could be applied, showing any workings that allow you to arrive at that rate

- reasons for the choice of depreciation method

Task 1.4

Tamworth Limited uses a budgeted overhead absorption rate based on labour hours. Data relating to the year ended 30 November 1996 is given in the table below and on page 186.

Complete the table below for the four production departments of the factory.

Note: round off your figures to the nearest £.

Department	Cutting	Moulding	Finishing	Packaging
Actual overheads incurred	£1,234,736	£1,156,347	£938,463	£834,674
Budgeted absorption rate per labour hour	£33.82	£26.80	£20.25	£29.62
Actual labour hours worked				
Overheads absorbed				
(Under)/over absorbed overheads				

REPORT

To:

From:

Subject: **Date:**

REPORT (continuation)

Task 1.5

Your assistant has taken a telephone call from the production manager, who has asked about the effectiveness of standard cost as a method of pricing material issues and valuing stock.

List some points below that will form the basis of a reply to the production manager. You should explain:

- what a standard material price represents

- how standard prices for materials will be ascertained

- the benefits and weaknesses of such a system

NOTES

SECTION 2

You are advised to spend approximately 45 minutes on this section.

2.1   Where would the information about workers leaving the company in Task 1.1 have come from?

....

....

2.2   The budgeted wage rate per hour for the finishing department is £5.10. Explain how this might have been arrived at.

....

....

....

....

....

2.3   List THREE indirect wage costs that might have been incurred in the packaging department.

....

....

....

2.4   The material used by the production departments of Tamworth Ltd would have come from the stores department, a service cost centre. Suggest how the costs for the stores department would be incorporated into product cost.

....

....

....

....

....

2.5 Activity-based costing has been put forward as a realistic alternative to more traditional methods of overhead absorption. Explain one way in which an activity-based costing (ABC) system differs from the more traditional methods of overhead absorption.

. . . .

. . . .

. . . .

. . . .

. . . .

. . . .

2.6 An order has been placed for a particular material that is used in the cutting department. The order delivery time could take from 2 to 4 weeks and the usage of the material fluctuates from a minimum of 3,000 units to a maximum of 5,000 units per week. Calculate the re-order level.

. . . .

. . . .

. . . .

. . . .

. . . .

. . . .

. . . .

2.7 The output of a process cost system will usually be reduced by normal loss and abnormal loss. Briefly explain the difference between the two and state how they will be treated in the accounts.

. . . .

. . . .

. . . .

. . . .

. . . .

2.8   Give an example of a cost centre from the data provided in Section 1 for Tamworth Ltd.

. . . .

. . . .

2.9   Overhead costs will either be allocated to a cost centre or apportioned to a cost centre.

(a)   Briefly explain the difference between the processes of allocation and apportionment.

. . . .

. . . .

. . . .

. . . .

. . . .

(b)   Give ONE example of:

(i)   an allocated overhead for the packaging department;

. . . .

(ii)   an apportioned overhead for the moulding department.

. . . .

2.10   The overheads for four production departments were under-absorbed by £151,977.

(a)   Does this mean actual overheads are less than absorbed overheads?

. . . .

. . . .

(b)   What effect will this under-absorption have on budgeted profit?

. . . .

. . . .

2.11 Explain the purpose of coding costs.

. . . .

. . . .

. . . .

. . . .

. . . .

. . . .

2.12 A company has the following details for the movement of an item of stock for November:

		Units	Cost per unit	Cost
			£	£
1 Nov	Opening balance	1,000	3.00	3,000
10 Nov	Receipts	1,200	3.50	4,200
25 Nov	Issues	1,800		

Complete the following table for FIFO and LIFO:

Date	Description	FIFO	LIFO
		£	£
25 Nov	Total issue value		
30 Nov	Total closing stock value		

This section has been added by Osborne Books to bring the Central Assessment tasks in line with the 1998 revisions to the Unit. The material is not AAT-sourced but Osborne Books copyright.

SECTION 3

You are advised to spend one hour on this section.

Lichfield Limited is another company within the same group as Tamworth Limited. Lichfield Limited makes a single product: bath salts provided in bulk to the trade. The materials supplied to the Lichfield factory need to be cleaned and mixed.

DATA

Standard costs for November 1996 for 1kg of bath salts:

Materials	1.25kgs at £2 per kilo	=	£2.50
Labour	0.5hrs at £7.50 per hour	=	£3.75
Fixed overheads	0.5hrs at £20 per hour	=	£10.00
TOTAL			£16.25

Fixed production overheads are absorbed on a standard labour hour basis. The budgeted production for November 1996 was 1,500kgs bath salts (completed).

The actual figures for November 1996 were as follows:

Production of the finished bath salts	1,700 kg
Cost of materials used (2,000 kgs)	£5,500
Labour cost (900 hours)	£6,300
Fixed overheads cost	£16,000

Task 3.1

Calculate the following variances:

(a)   material usage and price variances

(b)   labour efficiency and wage-rate variances

(c)   fixed overhead, expenditure, capacity, efficiency, and volume variances

Task 3.2

Complete the variance schedule on the next page.

Task 3.3

Complete the report on the next page, explaining the possible relationship between the material price and usage variance and how the overhead variance relates to over or under absorption of fixed overheads.

VARIANCE SCHEDULE

Lichfield Limited   **November 1996**

		£	£
Material Variance			
Material Usage			
Material Price			
TOTAL			
Labour Variance			
Labour Efficiency			
Labour Wage Rate			
TOTAL			
Fixed Overhead Variance			
Expenditure			
	Capacity		
	Efficiency		
Volume			
TOTAL			

REPORT

continue your report on a separate sheet of paper if necessary

Central Assessment Tasks

Bramwell Limited

The tasks in Sections 1 and 2 of this Central Assessment were issued by AAT in June 1997. Following the introduction of the revised Unit 5 'Recording Cost Information' in 1998, Osborne Books has added a new Section 3 covering the expansion of the specifications.

The tasks in Sections 1 and 2 are reproduced by kind permission of AAT.

The tasks in Section 3 have been provided by Roger Petheram.

It is recommended that students spend three hours completing the tasks, allocating the time as follows:

Section 1	75 minutes
Section 2	45 minutes
Section 3	60 minutes

Please note that from December 1999 the Central Assessment for this Unit will be set out in two sections. The content and approach remain the same.

SECTION 1

It is recommended that you spend approximately 1 hour 15 minutes on this section.

DATA

You are an accounting technician working in the cost office of Bramwell Limited, a company specialising in the production of confectionery. You report to the cost accountant who in turn reports to the production manager. The company's operations consist of the following production departments:

- processing

- quality assurance

- packing

The production departments are supported by the following service departments:

- stores

- factory maintenance

Bramwell Ltd operates a budgetary control system and uses standard costing.

You have been given a number of tasks to do in your office.

Task 1.1

The following budgeted figures for the next year are given to you for a new bar called 'Snick-Snack' at a full level of production of 6,000,000 bars.

	£
Direct Material	300,000
Direct Labour	250,000
Direct Expenses	200,000
Prime Cost	750,000
Variable Overheads	150,000
Fixed Overheads	300,000
Total Cost	1,200,000

(a)   Demand for the product is uncertain so the cost accountant has asked you to complete the following table for the account manager of Snick-Snack, detailing costs per bar at the different levels of production.

Production (bars)	5,400,000	5,700,000	6,000,000
% of Capacity	90%	95%	100%
Costs	£	£	£
Direct Material			300,000
Direct Labour			250,000
Direct Expenses			200,000
Prime Cost			750,000
Variable Overheads			150,000
Fixed Overheads			300,000
Total Cost			1,200,000
Total Cost Per Bar (to 4 decimal places)			0.2000

(b)   The account manager is surprised at the movement in the cost per bar.

Using the stationery below write a short memorandum:

- outlining the trend in cost per bar over the range of production

- explaining the reason for this trend

MEMORANDUM

To:

From:

Subject: **Date:**

Task 1.2

The cost accountant is concerned about the cost of biscuit used in the manufacture of a long-established product by the name of 'Nutbite' for period 11. He has arranged a meeting with the production manager to discuss this and has asked you to review the results for period 11.

Results for period 11 are:

Actual Production	850,000 bars
Actual Biscuit Usage	93,500 kgs
Actual Cost of Biscuit Usage	£40,205

The budget set out the following data:

Standard Price per Kilo of Biscuit	£0.415
Standard Usage @ Production Level of 850,000 bars	89,250 kgs

Use the stationery on the next page to:

*   detail the variances for period 11

*   offer possible reasons for the causes of these variances

Note: show your answers to the nearest £.

REPORT TITLE: ....

PERIOD: ....

        Material price variance (£)

        Material usage variance (£)   ————————

        Total material cost variance (£)   ————————

POSSIBLE REASONS FOR THE CAUSES OF THESE VARIANCES

Task 1.3

At a meeting between you, the cost accountant and the production manager, doubts were raised about the efficiency of labour and the increased cost implications. A general discussion followed about the introduction of a bonus scheme, whereby direct labour personnel would be given a bonus of 50% of standard hours saved, paid at a basic rate of pay. However, the production manager has a number of reservations about how such a bonus scheme could:

    (i)   encourage direct labour to work more efficiently

    (ii)   save money for the company

At the end of the meeting you have been asked to write a report (using the stationery on the next two pages) which:

- outlines the characteristics of a bonus scheme that operates as a percentage of standard hours saved

- explains the incentives that will be given to direct labour to work more efficiently using the figures given below

- indicates how such a bonus scheme would increase profitability for the company

- highlights any concerns that you may want addressed for the effective implementation of such a bonus scheme

For the basis of the report you may assume that an average member of the direct labour personnel working 35 hours a week at a basic rate of £6.00 per hour would produce 168 units. Each unit has a standard production time allowance of 15 minutes.

REPORT

To:

From:

Subject: **Date:**

REPORT (continuation)

Task 1.4

The cost accountant has given you the task of preparing a budgeted production overhead schedule for the company. You are given the following data to assist you.

	Total	Processing	Quality Assurance	Packing	Stores	Factory Maintenance
Number of Personnel	650	440	40	100	40	30
Area (sq ft)	100,000	52,000	16,000	10,000	10,000	12,000
Machine Usage (hours)	65,000	45,000	2,000	18,000		
Number of Material Requisitions	11,000	6,260	2,450	1,290		1,000
Number of Maintenance Hours	50,000	32,000	4,000	14,000		

You are required to complete the following overhead analysis schedule using appropriate bases of apportionment from the data given on the previous page.

BUDGETED PRODUCTION OVERHEAD SCHEDULE

Overhead	Basis	Total £	Processing £	Quality Assurance £	Packing £	Stores £	Factory Maintenance £
Rent & Rates		320,000					
Canteen Costs		169,000					
Depreciation of Machinery		273,000					
Total		762,000					

SECTION 2

You are advised to spend approximately 45 minutes on this section.

2.1   Bramwell Ltd has a policy of holding a buffer stock for most of the stock that it purchases. Explain what a 'buffer stock' is.

. . . .

. . . .

. . . .

. . . .

. . . .

2.2   Bramwell Ltd uses standard costing. Explain what this means for stock issues and stock valuation.

. . . .

. . . .

. . . .

. . . .

. . . .

2.3   The production manager is considering using FIFO or LIFO for pricing issues and stock valuation. Explain the costing differences between these two methods.

. . . .

. . . .

. . . .

. . . .

. . . .

2.4   In Task 1.3 you wrote a report about the implementation of a bonus scheme for Bramwell Ltd.

(a)   In a bonus scheme is it budgeted labour hours or standard labour hours produced which are used to help calculate a bonus?

....

(b)   Explain the difference between budgeted labour hours and standard labour hours produced.

....

....

....

....

2.5   In Task 1.1 you were given a task concerning fixed costs and variable costs in Bramwell Ltd. Sketch in the graphs below how fixed costs and variable costs behave with changes in the level of activity.

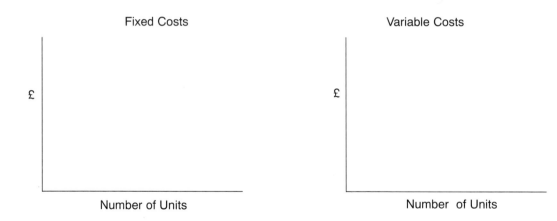

2.6   In Task 1.4 you were given a task on apportionment of overheads in Bramwell Ltd. Explain the difference between the apportionment and absorption of overheads.

....

....

....

....

2.7   In Task 1.4 you were asked to calculate a budgeted production overhead schedule for Bramwell Ltd.

(a)   Outline what now needs to be done with the budgeted costs of the service departments in order to arrive at overhead absorption rates for the production departments.

. . . .

. . . .

. . . .

. . . .

(b)   Explain the reasons for your recommended action in (a) above.

. . . .

. . . .

. . . .

. . . .

2.8   Last year Quality Assurance Department underabsorbed £15,000 of overheads. Explain what this means.

. . . .

. . . .

. . . .

. . . .

. . . .

2.9   Bramwell Ltd uses a process costing system rather than a job costing system. Explain why this is the case.

. . . .

. . . .

....

....

....

....

2.10 During period 11, for one of the products made by Bramwell Ltd, 4,000kgs of biscuit were input into the process and the output from the process was 3,700 kgs. Budgeted normal loss is 5%.

(a) Identify the normal and abnormal loss of this process by kg.

....

....

....

....

(b) Give the book-keeping entry for any abnormal loss.

....

....

....

....

2.11 Identify the double entry for the material usage variance that you calculated in Task 1.2.

Account	DR (£)	CR (£)
....	....	....
....	....	....
....	....	....
....	....	....

This section has been added by Osborne Books to bring the Central Assessment tasks in line with the 1998 revisions to the Unit. The material is not AAT-sourced but Osborne Books copyright.

SECTION 3

You are advised to spend one hour on this section.

Another company from the same group as Bramwell Limited is Axedown Ltd. This company produces biscuits for the local tourist trade. The costing data is as follows:

Standard costs for a tin of biscuits:

Materials (2kgs of ingredients)	=	£2.50
Labour (0.25 hours)	=	£2.00
Fixed Overheads	=	£3.00
TOTAL PRODUCTION COST	=	£7.50

Notes • the fixed overheads are absorbed on a standard labour hour

• the budgeted hours for the period were 2000 standard hours, ie 8000 tins of biscuits

Actual data for the period:

Output was 7,500 tins of biscuits.

Costs:

Materials cost (16,000kgs)	£19,200
Labour cost (1,800 hours)	£15,300
Fixed overheads	£24,000
TOTAL PRODUCTION COST	£58,500

Task 3.1

Calculate the following variances:

(a) material usage and price variances

(b) labour efficiency and wage-rate variances

(c) fixed overhead, expenditure, capacity, efficiency, and volume variances

Task 3.2

Complete the variance schedule on the next page.

Task 3.3

Prepare a report explaining the causes of adverse variances for material and labour variances. For each cause identify a course of corrective action.

VARIANCE SCHEDULE

Axedown Limited   **June 1997**

		£	£
Material Variance			
Material Usage			
Material Price			
TOTAL			
Labour Variance			
Labour Efficiency			
Labour Wage Rate			
TOTAL			
Fixed Overhead Variance			
Expenditure			
	Capacity		
	Efficiency		
Volume			
TOTAL			

REPORT

continue your report on a separate sheet of paper if necessary

Central Assessment Tasks

Gilbert Mouldings

The tasks in Sections 1 and 2 of this Central Assessment were issued by AAT in December 1997. Following the introduction of the revised Unit 5 'Recording Cost Information' in 1998, Osborne Books has added a new Section 3 covering the expansion of the specifications.

Tasks in Sections 1 and 2 are reproduced by kind permission of AAT.

The tasks in Section 3 have been provided by Roger Petheram.

It is recommended that students spend three hours completing the tasks, allocating the time as follows:

Section 1	75 minutes
Section 2	45 minutes
Section 3	60 minutes

Please note that from December 1999 the Central Assessment for this Unit will be set out in two sections. The content and approach remain the same.

SECTION 1

You are recommended to spend approximately 1 hour 15 minutes on this section.

DATA

You are an accounting technician working in the cost office of Gilbert Mouldings Ltd, a company that uses a job costing system. You are reviewing the work of a cost clerk who has completed a number of tasks on Job 548, which has been undertaken at a small subsidiary factory of the company. The factory is a separate cost centre and cost accounts are prepared at each month end. Job 548 was the only job undertaken during the month of November 1997 at the factory and it was both started and finished within the month.

Task 1.1

The cost clerk has provided you with a table (see page 220) showing the issues of material Bitcom to Job 548 for the month of November 1997. Material Bitcom was used only on Job 548 during this period and the *first-in-first-out* method has been used for costing the issues and valuing stock.

You have decided that *last-in-first-out* is the most appropriate method for costing the issues of material Bitcom to Job 548.

(a)   Using the table on page 221, cost the issues and value the stock of material Bitcom on a *last-in-first-out* basis.

(b)   Write a short memo to the cost clerk, using the stationery provided on the next page, explaining:

(i)   the main differences between FIFO and LIFO costing methods

(ii)   the consequences of the change in policy for Job 548 and the stock of material Bitcom

MEMORANDUM

To:

From:

Subject: **Date:**

MATERIAL BITCOM

JOB: **548**   MONTH: **NOV 97**

Date	Receipts			Issues			Stock		
	Quantity (Units)	Unit Price £	Value £	Quantity (Units)	Unit Price £	Value £	Quantity (Units)	Unit Price £	Value £
Bal 1 Nov							50	40	2,000
2 Nov	450	50	22,500				500	(50 × 40) (450 × 50)	24,500
6 Nov				240	(50 × 40) (190 × 50)	11,500	260	50	13,000
12 Nov	360	60	21,600				620	(260 × 50) (360 × 60)	34,600
14 Nov				290	(260 × 50) (30 × 60)	14,800	330	60	19,800
20 Nov	300	90	27,000				630	(330 × 60) (300 × 90)	46,800
23 Nov				320	60	19,200	310	(10 × 60) (300 × 90)	27,600
30 Nov				280	(10 × 60) (270 × 90)	24,900	30	90	2,700

MATERIAL BITCOM								
JOB: **548**					MONTH: **NOV 97**			
Date	**Receipts**			**Issues**			**Stock**		
	Quantity (Units)	Unit Price £	Value £	Quantity (Units)	Unit Price £	Value £	Quantity (Units)	Unit Price £	Value £
Bal 1 Nov							50	40	2,000
2 Nov	450	50	22,500				500		
6 Nov				240			260		
12 Nov	360	60	21,600				620		
14 Nov				290			330		
20 Nov	300	90	27,000				630		
23 Nov				320			310		
30 Nov				280			30		

Task 1.2

The cost clerk has collected the following data about direct labour costs for Job 548 for November 1997:

Standard wage rate per direct labour hour	£8.50
Standard labour cost	£35,700
Actual direct labour hours worked	4,160 hrs
Actual direct labour cost	£38,480

One category of labour was used and one standard wage rate payment was budgeted for.

Using the stationery set out below:

(i) calculate the labour variances for November 1997

(ii) briefly offer possible causes of the labour efficiency variance and the labour wage rate variance

---

LABOUR VARIANCE REPORT

JOB: . . . . .PERIOD: . . . .

£

Labour efficiency variance

Labour wage rate variance _____

Labour cost variance _____

Task 1.3

The cost clerk has asked for your assistance in completing a job cost card for Job 548.

You are told that:

*   Bitcom was the only material used on Job 548 and it is to be costed on a LIFO basis as calculated in Task 1.1

*   direct labour costs are as reported in Task 1.2

*   direct expenses comprise of 195 hours of machine hire which cost £15 per hour

*   production overheads are absorbed on the basis of direct labour hours

*   administration overheads are absorbed on the basis of a third of total production cost

*   Total Budgeted Production overheads for the year for the factory are £1,324,925

*   Total Budgeted Direct Labour Hours for the year for the factory are 58,625

Complete the job cost card using the stationery below.

JOB COST CARD	
JOB:	MONTH:
	£
Direct Material	
Direct Labour	
Direct Expenses	
Production Overhead	
PRODUCTION COST	
Administration Overhead	
TOTAL COST	
Profit (a third of Job Price)	
JOB PRICE	

Task 1.4

The cost clerk has identified overheads incurred for the factory at which Job 548 was completed.

Using the stationery below:

(i) complete the following table using the information you have compiled in Task 1.3

(ii) write brief notes that explain your results and the effect on the profitability of Job 548

OVERHEAD SUMMARY

MONTH: NOVEMBER 1997   **COST CENTRE: JOB 548**

	Overhead Absorbed	Overhead Incurred	(Under)/Over Absorption of Overhead
	£	£	£
Production Overhead		99,328	
Administration Overhead		74,269	

NOTES

SECTION 2

You are advised to spend approximately 45 minutes on this section.

2.1 The company in Section 1 uses a job costing system for Job 548. Identify one reason why job costing would be used.

....

....

....

2.2 Two of the costs outlined in the job cost card in Task 1.3 are direct expenses and production overheads. Give TWO examples of direct expenses and production overhead that might relate to Job 548.

Direct Expenses   (i)   ....

                                  ....

                         (ii)   ....

                                  ....

Production Overheads   (i)   ....

                         (ii)   ....

2.3 In Task 1.3 production overheads were absorbed on a direct labour hour basis. State another method of overhead absorption which is based upon time.

....

2.4 Explain why a method of overhead absorption based on time is considered more appropriate than a method based upon monetary value, eg percentage of labour cost.

....

....

....

....

2.5 Explain the difference between a material requisition and a purchase requisition with particular reference to the material Bitcom used in Job 548.

....

....

....

....

....

2.6 You are told that the lead time for material Bitcom is 10 days and the buffer stock is 25 units. Explain what this means.

....

....

....

....

2.7 The stores department is responsible for a stocktake.

(a) Explain what a stocktake is.

....

....

....

(b) State two methods by which the stocktaking process can be carried out.

(i) ....

(ii) ....

2.8   (a)   Calculate the standard hours saved on Job 548 using the data from Task 1.2.

. . . .

. . . .

. . . .

. . . .

. . . .

. . . .

(b)   Assume that the direct workers on Job 548 were paid a bonus equal to 75% of standard hours saved at actual basic wage rate. Calculate the total labour bonus payment on Job 548 for November 1997.

. . . .

. . . .

. . . .

. . . .

. . . .

. . . .

. . . .

2.9   Task 1.2 used a standard wage rate of £8.50 per labour hour. List two factors that might have been taken into account in arriving at a standard wage rate.

(i)   . . . .

. . . .

(ii)   . . . .

. . . .

2.10 (a) Explain what idle time is.

....

....

....

....

(b) Give TWO causes of idle time.

(i) ....

(ii) ....

2.11 Complete the account below using your figures from Task 1.4 as at the end of November 1997.

Under/over absorbed Overheads Account

This section has been added by Osborne Books to bring the Central Assessment tasks in line with the 1998 revisions to the Unit. The material is not AAT-sourced but Osborne Books copyright.

SECTION 3

You are advised to spend one hour on this section.

You have been given cost information in relation to Job 549 which was completed in the Wyevale factory in the last week of November 1997. This was the only Job started and finished in the week.

Standard costs for Job 549

Materials:	Byrite	10kg	=	£20 per kg
	Extet	12kg	=	£25 per kg
Labour cost:		360 hours	=	£8.50 per hour

Fixed overheads are absorbed on a standard labour hour basis at a rate of £22 per labour hour.

Budgeted hours for the week were 390 hours. Remember that this was the only job started and finished in the week.

Actual costs for Job 549

Materials:	Byrite	12kgs	£260
	Extet	13kgs	£400
Labour		400hrs	£3,600
Fixed overheads incurred			£6,000
TOTAL			£10,260

Task 3.1

Calculate the following variances:

(a)   material usage and price variance for each material

(b)   labour efficiency and wage-rate variances

(c)   fixed overhead, expenditure, capacity, efficiency, and volume variances

Task 3.2

Complete the variance schedule on the next page.

Task 3.3

Complete the report highlighting variances over £500. Discuss the possible reasons for material and labour variances and explain the reason for the over/under absorption of fixed overheads.

VARIANCE SCHEDULE

Job 549   **November 1997**

		£	£
Material Variance			
Byrite	Material Usage		
	Material Price		
Extet	Material Usage		
	Material Price		
TOTAL			
Labour Variance			
Labour Efficiency			
Labour Wage Rate			
TOTAL			
Fixed Overhead Variance			
Expenditure			
	Capacity		
	Efficiency		
Volume			
TOTAL			

REPORT

continue your report on a separate sheet of paper if necessary

Central Assessment Tasks

Wickford Limited

This series of Central Assessment tasks was issued by AAT in 1998 to provide guidance for the revised Unit 5 'Recording Cost Information'.

The tasks in all sections are reproduced by kind permission of AAT.

It is recommended that students spend three hours completing the tasks, allocating the time as follows:

Section 1	75 minutes
Section 2	45 minutes
Section 3	60 minutes

Please note that from December 1999 the Central Assessment for this Unit will be set out in two sections. The content and approach remain the same.

SECTION 1

You are advised to spend approximately 1 hour 15 minutes on this section.

Please note that the tasks should be attempted in numerical order.

DATA

Wickford Limited is a company that specialises in the manufacture of crystal glass. It makes a number of standard products, for which there is a buoyant demand, and also makes one-off products. One such one-off product is a commemorative vase to celebrate one hundred and fifty years of glass-making within the factory.

The manufacturing process within the factory is organised into three production cost centres, which are:

- Blowing
- Cutting
- Engraving

These production cost centres are serviced by three service cost centres, which are:

- Quality control
- Stores
- Maintenance

You are an accounting technician working in the cost department and you report to the cost accountant. You have been given a number of tasks concerned with the factory's activities for 1997 and its plans for 1998.

Task 1.1

Your office has been given the responsibility of compiling the budgeted costs for the commemorative vase. Initially, production was forecast at 750,000 units; however, overseas interest now means that demand could be as high as 1,000,000 or 1,250,000 units.

Complete the budgeted cost schedule below for 1,000,000 and 1,250,000 units.

	1998 BUDGETED PRODUCTION COSTS		
UNITS / **COSTS**	**750,000**	**1,000,000**	**1,250,000**
VARIABLE COSTS	£	£	£
Material	2,250,000		
Labour	2,437,500		
Overhead	2,062,500		
Total	6,750,000		
FIXED COSTS			
Labour	1,100,000		
Overhead	1,750,000		
Total	2,850,000		
TOTAL PRODUCTION COST	9,600,000		
COST PER UNIT	12.80		

Task 1.2

Labour in the blowing department is organised into teams of three. For the manufacture of the commemorative vase there will be a master blower, blower and a general assistant in each team.

You are told that the following rates of pay apply in the blowing department:

Master blower	£8.60 per hour
Blower	£6.40 per hour
General assistant	£4.20 per hour

Standards set for the production of the commemorative vase are that each team should produce 30 vases per hour. In order to encourage production, it has been agreed that each member of the team should receive a bonus of 50% of any time saved, paid at the standard rate.

During January 1998, Team Alpha in the blowing department produced 5,370 vases. Team Alpha worked four five-day weeks in January 1998 and each working day was seven and three-quarters hours.

Complete the wage schedule below to determine the total pay for each member of Team Alpha for January 1998.

WAGE SCHEDULE

Blowing Department: Team Alpha   **Month:** January 1998

	Team	Master Blower	Blower	General Assistant
Wage Rate (£)				
Hours worked				
Total Wage (£)				
Standard Hours Produced				
Standard Hours Saved				
Bonus (£)				
Total Wage + Bonus (£)				

Task 1.3

The raw materials that are used in the manufacture of the commemorative crystal vase are silica sand, potash and lead monoxide. The company has noted that the cost of silica sand from suppliers fluctuates and it needs to ensure that it issues the sand to production at a cost that reflects the most recent price.

Complete the store card below using the *last-in-first-out* costing method to cost issues of silica sand and value stock for the month of November 1997.

STORE CARD

Material: Silica Sand **Month:** November 1997

DATE	RECEIPTS			ISSUES			STOCK		
Nov	Qty kilos 000s	Cost per kilo £	Value £000	Qty kilos 000s	Cost per kilo £	Value £000	Qty kilos 000s	Cost per kilo £	Value £000
1 (Bal)							1,470	2.00	2,940
5	860	2.15							
9				1,060					
14	1,100	2.25							
18	1,050	2.20							
21				2,300					
23	1,430	2.40							
25				1,540					
28				820					

Task 1.4

It has been decided that production overheads will be charged to the commemorative vases on the basis of the pre-determined production overhead rates for each of the production cost centres.

You are given the following budgeted information for 1998:

- The production departments (blowing, cutting and engraving) are serviced by the quality control, stores and maintenance departments.

- The maintenance department will provide the following service hours to the other departments for 1998:

Blowing	1,400
Cutting	725
Engraving	475
Quality Control	240
Stores	240

- The stores department is budgeted to receive the following requisitions orders from the other cost centres:

Blowing	1,944
Cutting	712
Engraving	524
Quality Control	172

- The quality control department is budgeted to provide the following hours of service to the production cost centres:

Blowing	6,300
Cutting	2,100
Engraving	1,800

- Production overheads will be absorbed on a labour hour basis.

(a) Complete the budgeted production overhead schedule below to reapportion the service department overheads and calculate the total budgeted overheads for the three production departments. Ignore variable overheads.

Year: 1998	Budgeted Production Overhead Schedule						
Cost Centre / Cost	Blowing £000	Cutting £000	Engraving £000	Quality Control £000	Stores £000	Mainten- ance £000	Total £000
Allocated Overhead	876	534	413	278	374	292	2,767
Apportioned Overhead	1,138	793	541	311	416	324	3,523
Sub-total	**2,014**	**1,327**	**954**	**589**	**790**	**616**	**6,290**
Maintenance							
Stores							
Quality Control							
Total Budgeted Overheads							

(b)   Complete the following table.

	Blowing	Cutting	Engraving
Total Budgeted Overheads (£)	3,200,000	1,790,000	1,300,000
Budgeted labour hours	48,000	35,800	32,500
Budgeted Overhead Absorption Rate £ (per labour hour)			

Note: show the budgeted overhead absorption rate to two decimal places.

It is envisaged that each commemorative vase will spend the following times in the production cost centres.

	Blowing	Cutting	Engraving
Labour time (mins)	9	7.5	12

(c)   Complete the following table to show the production overhead to be absorbed by each vase.

Department	Time (minutes)	Budgeted Overhead Absorption Rate per labour hour £	Overhead Absorbed £
Blowing			
Cutting			
Engraving			
Total			

SECTION 2

You are advised to spend 45 minutes on this section.

2.1 Briefly describe and explain the trend in costs per unit for the three budgeted levels of production in Task 1.1.

. . . .

. . . .

. . . .

. . . .

. . . .

. . . .

. . . .

. . . .

2.2 Sketch in the graphs below to show how fixed and variable costs behave in general with changes in the level of production.

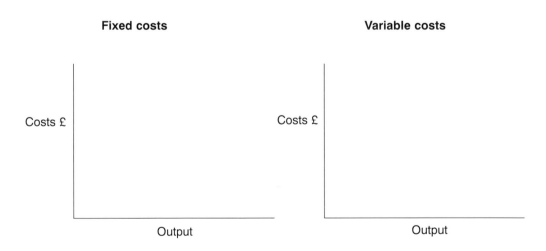

Fixed costs   **Variable costs**

Costs £   Costs £

Output   Output

2.3   The cost schedule in Task 1.1 defined overhead costs as being either fixed or variable with changes in the level of activity.

Give ONE other classification of behaviour of overhead cost and an example of an overhead cost that matches this classification. Then sketch a graph to show how the cost behaves with changes in the level of activity.

Classification. . . . .

Example . . . .

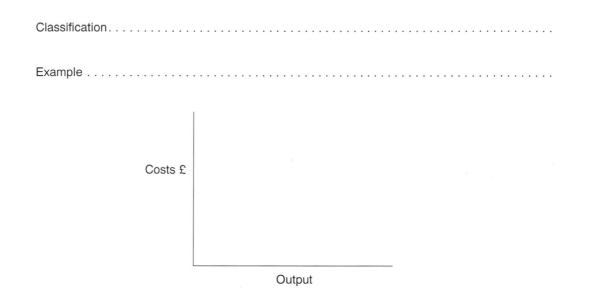

2.4   Briefly explain the benefits of a bonus scheme to workers and employers.

(a)   Benefits to workers

. . . .

. . . .

. . . .

. . . .

(b)   Benefits to employers

. . . .

. . . .

. . . .

. . . .

2.5 In order to introduce a bonus in Task 1.2, it was necessary to establish standard times of production. Briefly explain how these standard times for the blowing team will have been established.

. . . .

. . . .

. . . .

. . . .

. . . .

2.6 Wickford Limited wants to identify periods of absence in the blowing department during 1998. Identify TWO documents that will provide this information.

(i) . . . .

(ii) . . . .

2.7 Explain why L.I.F.O. was chosen as the method to cost issues of silica sand in Task 1.3.

. . . .

. . . .

. . . .

. . . .

2.8 Briefly highlight the weaknesses of the L.I.F.O. method of costing issues and valuing stock.

. . . .

. . . .

. . . .

. . . .

. . . .

2.9   The company carries a large volume of silica sand, potash and lead monoxide and is concerned about the costs of holding and ordering stock.

List TWO costs of holding stock and TWO costs of ordering stock.

Holding Cost   Ordering Cost

(i) . . . .   (i) . . . .

(ii) . . . .   (ii) . . . .

2.10   (a)   Identify a method that the company could use to minimise the costs listed in Task 2.9 above.

. . . .

(b)   Briefly explain what this method sets out to achieve.

. . . .

. . . .

. . . .

. . . .

. . . .

. . . .

2.11   Task 1.4 shows allocated overheads and apportioned overheads for each cost centre. Give one example of each type for the blowing department.

Blowing department allocated overhead . . . .

Blowing department apportioned overhead . . . .

2.12 Briefly explain the reasons for your choice of allocated and apportioned overheads for the blowing department in Task 2.11.

. . . .

. . . .

. . . .

. . . .

. . . .

. . . .

. . . .

SECTION 3

You are advised to spend approximately one hour on this section.

Task 3.1

You have been given the task of reviewing the performance of the blowing department for the month of January 1998. Variances for material and labour have been calculated by a cost clerk in your office and are shown in the table on page 235.

The fixed overhead variances have not been calculated but you have ascertained the following information for the blowing department for January 1998:

Budgeted overheads	£217,750
Budgeted hours	3,250
Budgeted overhead absorption rate	£67 per labour hour
Actual overheads	£234,270
Actual hours worked	3,100
Standard hours produced	3,180

You have been told that the material used in the blowing department has been acquired from new suppliers as the company is concerned to keep costs under control and the new supplier's prices were cheaper.

The company had budgeted for a small cost-of-living wage increase to be implemented in January 1998; however, this had been renegotiated to a figure that was almost double the original rise.

Complete the table of variances and prepare a report, using the stationery on the next page. The table and the analysis in the report should:

- summarise the variances for material, labour and overheads and note any significant sub-variance in excess of £4,000

- highlight the causes of all material and labour variances from information given

- derive the under/over-absorption of overheads from the variances calculated and explain how the under/over-absorption has come about

VARIANCE SCHEDULE

Blowing Department   **January 1998**

		£	£
Material Variance			
Material Usage			4,236 (A)
Material Price			1,125 (F)
TOTAL			3,111 (A)
Labour Variance			
Labour Efficiency			1,750 (F)
Labour Wage Rate			5,865 (A)
TOTAL			4,115 (A)
Fixed Overhead Variance			
Expenditure			
	Capacity		
	Efficiency		
Volume			
TOTAL			

REPORT

continue your report on a separate sheet of paper if necessary

appendix
document formats

the structure of a total cost statement and a profit statement

	TOTAL COST STATEMENT	
		£
	Direct materials	x
add	Direct labour	x
add	Direct expenses	x
equals	PRIME COST	x
add	Production overheads	x
equals	PRODUCTION COST	x
add	Selling and distribution costs	x
add	Administration costs — non-production overheads	x
add	Finance costs	x
equals	TOTAL COST	x

	PROFIT STATEMENT	
		£
	Sales	x
less	Total cost	x
equals	PROFIT	x

the structure of a manufacturing account and a profit and loss account

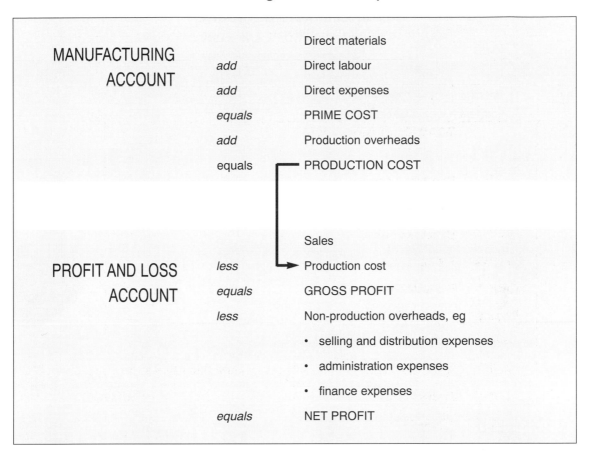

MANUFACTURING ACCOUNT

	Direct materials
add	Direct labour
add	Direct expenses
equals	PRIME COST
add	Production overheads
equals	PRODUCTION COST

PROFIT AND LOSS ACCOUNT

	Sales
less	Production cost
equals	GROSS PROFIT
less	Non-production overheads, eg
	• selling and distribution expenses
	• administration expenses
	• finance expenses
equals	NET PROFIT

an example of a manufacturing and profit and loss account

ALPHA MANUFACTURING COMPANY
MANUFACTURING AND PROFIT AND LOSS ACCOUNT
for the year ended 31 December 1999

	£	£
Opening stock of direct materials		5,000
Add Purchases of direct materials		50,000
		55,000
Less Closing stock of direct materials		6,000
COST OF DIRECT MATERIALS USED		49,000
Direct labour		26,000
Direct expenses		2,500
PRIME COST		77,500
Add Production (factory) overheads:		
Indirect materials	2,000	
Indirect labour	16,000	
Indirect expenses:		
Rent of factory	5,000	
Depreciation of factory machinery	10,000	
Factory light and heat	4,000	
		37,000
		114,500
Add Opening stock of work-in-progress		4,000
		118,500
Less Closing stock of work-in-progress		3,000
PRODUCTION COST OF GOODS COMPLETED		115,500
Sales		195,500
Opening stock of finished goods	6,500	
Production cost of goods completed	115,500	
	122,000	
Less Closing stock of finished goods	7,500	
COST OF SALES		114,500
Gross profit		81,000
Less Non-production overheads:		
Selling and distribution expenses	38,500	
Administration expenses	32,000	
Finance expenses	3,500	
		74,000
Net profit		7,000